THE CHARLTON STANDARD CATALOGUE OF

ROYAL WORCESTER ANIMALS

MILLENNIUM EDITION

BY
JOHN EDWARDS

W. K. CROSS
PUBLISHER

The Charlton Press

PALM HARBOR, FLORIDA • TORONTO, ONTARIO

Canadian Cataloguing in Publication Data

Edwards, John, 1944-

The Charlton standard catalogue of Royal Worcester animals

Includes index.

ISBN 0-88968-242-9
1. Royal Worcester figurines—Catalogs. 2. Porcelain animals—Catalogs. I. Title. II. Title: Royal Worcester animals.

NK4395.E38 2001 738.8'2'029442 C00-901522-1

Printed in Canada
in the Province of Manitoba

EDITORIAL TEAM

Editor	Jean Dale
Assistant Editor	Cindy Raycroft
Graphic Technician	Davina Rowan

ACKNOWLEDGEMENTS

The Charlton Press and the author would like to thank all those who have helped with the first edition of *The Charlton Standard Catalogue of Royal Worcester Animals.*

Contributors to the First Edition

A special thank you to Tony Cast, West Yorkshire, England, who is the co-author of *The Charlton Standard Catalogue of Royal Worcester Figurines*, and whose original work five years ago certainly helped us on our way.

Also a special thanks to Wendy Cook, Curator of The Museum of Worcester Porcelain, for her patience in putting up with all our questions, and her assistance in adding the finishing touches on, and proofing, the final manuscript.

Also thanks to the staff at Royal Worcester, especially Elizabeth Greenshields; Amanda Savidge; Helen Sinden; Ted Taylor; Nettie Wade.

Also thanks to collectors John Andrews; Jo Ellen Arnold; Gabrielle Doherty Bullock of Bygones of Worcester; Jennifer Campbell; Joseph Carr; Patrick Cerra; Freda and Jim Edmunds; Harry Frost; Ron Heberlee; M. Langham; Glenda J. May, Bruce Kodner Galleries; Patricia Marsico and Jeanette Mostowicz, Mars-Most Antiques; Alan Pullen; Peggy Rowbottom; and Joseph Schenberg for all their assistance.

A SPECIAL NOTE TO COLLECTORS

We welcome and appreciate any comments or suggestions in regard to *The Charlton Standard Catalogue of Royal Worcester Animals.* If you would like to participate in pricing or supply previously unavailable data or information, please contact Jean Dale at (416) 488-1418, or e-mail us at chpress@charltonpress.com.

The Charlton Press

Editorial Office:

2040 Yonge Street, Suite 208, Toronto, Ontario M4S 1Z9

Telephone: (416) 488-1418 Fax: (416) 488-4656

Telephone: (800) 442-6042 Fax: (800) 442-1542

url: www.charltonpress.com; e-mail: chpress@charltonpress.com

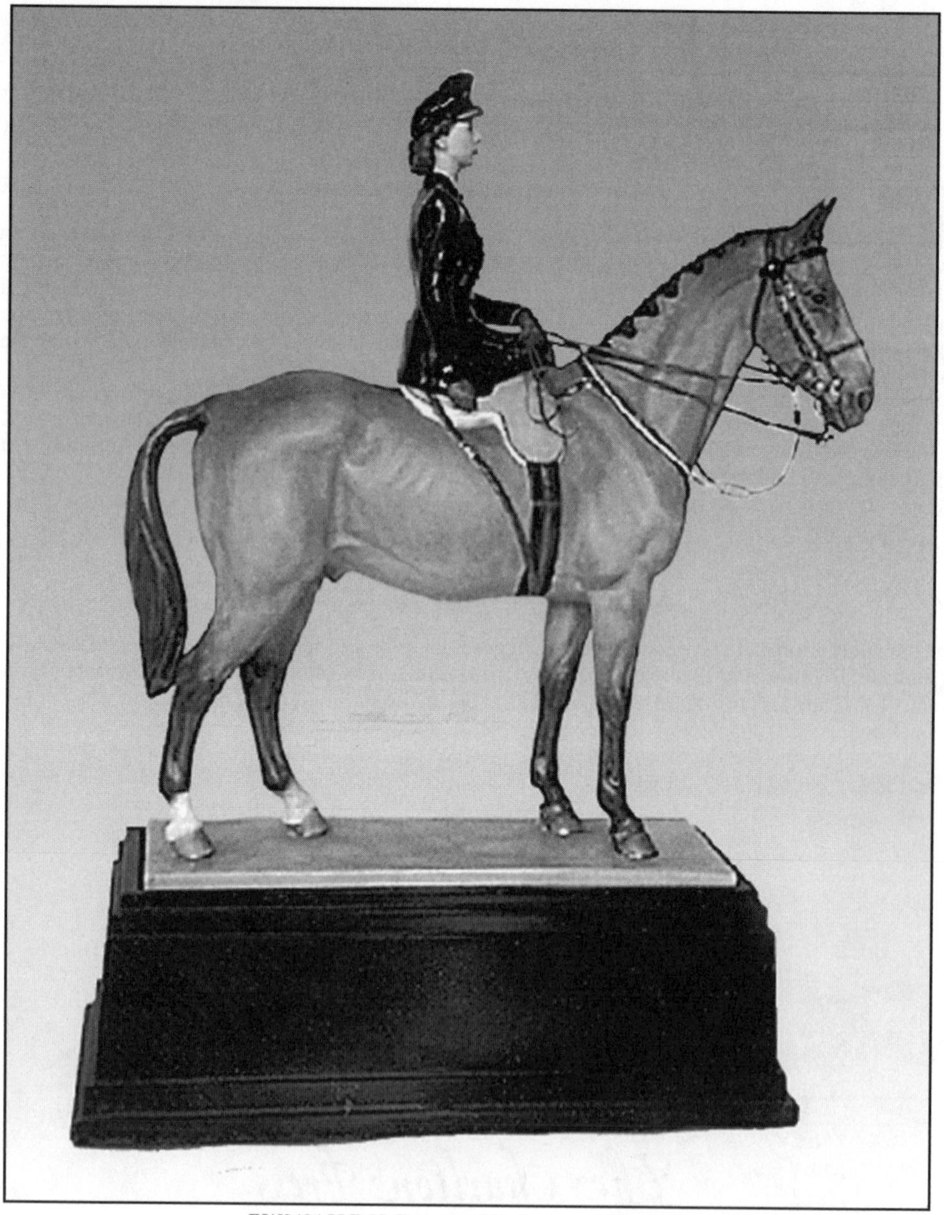

RW3434 H.R.H. Princess Elizabeth on "Tommy"

TABLE OF CONTENTS

RW2664 Parrot, Male (On stump)

INTRODUCTION

A HISTORY OF ROYAL WORCESTER

Porcelain, once an exorbitant luxury item exclusive to China, began production in Germany in 1711 (Meissen) and in the early eighteenth century in Italy and France (notably Sevres). Fifty years later it was manufactured in England, with factories developing in Shropshire, Derby, Plymouth, Bow, Lowestoft, Chelsea and Bristol, along with smaller operations scattered about Wales. The Worcester Tonquin Manufacture was formed in June 1751 by Dr. John Wall and fourteen other local businessmen, and is the oldest continually existing porcelain manufacturer in Britain. The newly formed company leased their first premises, Warmstry House, on the Severn in Worcester, and began making teapots and tableware.

Together with William Davis, an apothecary, Dr. Wall appears to have developed a soft-paste method using Cornish soapstone already in use at Benjamin Lund's factory at Bristol. Unlike its contemporaries, this formula made porcelain that would not crack when brought into contact with boiling water (the ingredients have remained largely unchanged over the past 250 years). The Worcester factories, along with similar operations in Caughley, Shropshire (called "Salop ware") and Liverpool, quickly surpassed the other outfits in sales of tea and dinner services.

While the Bow, Chelsea and Derby operations produce a number of figurines at that time on Continental models, the Worcester Porcelain Company concentrated on quality table ware. However, they and the Bristol plant (which merged with Worcester in 1752) did make a handful of unsophisticated figurines in their early years such as a white glazed Chinese man circa 1750. One early porcelain figure, "Cupid at Vulcan's Forge," was made at the Worcester factory in the 1760s. It is thought to be modelled by John Toulouse, who also produced some of the figurines made in the Worcester factory of Robert Chamberlain.

Dr. Wall retired in 1774 and died in 1776. William Davis was head of the factory until his death in 1783, whereupon the firm was purchased by the company's London agent, Thomas Flight. In 1789, following a visit to the factory by King George III and Queen Charlotte, the King granted the factory a Royal Warrant, hence the term "Royal Worcester." A London showroom was also opened at His Majesty's suggestion. The factory has continued to enjoy Royal Warrants until this day. Flight, together with his sons John and Joseph and various other family members, ran the Worcester factory until the 1840s, with the involvement of the Barr family, selling mostly tableware. At this time they merged with Chamberlain's factory. The operations were then moved from Warmstry house to Diglis, the site of Chamberlain's works, where the present factory stands. In 1851 the company was purchased by W. H. Kerr and R. W. Binns. The two men introduced Parian (a semi-matte material high in feldspar), first used by the Copeland factory in the 1840s, to the Worcester factory. This material was more lasting and easily coloured or gilded than earlier formulas, making it more suitable for the detailed modelling with which the name Worcester is now synonymous. This lead to an unpredecented expansion in both production of and demand for figurines, especially after the company issued stock and started trading as Worcester Royal Porcelain Company Ltd. in 1862.

The company also started hiring trained sculptors such as W. B. Kirk, E. J. Jones, and Charles Toft rather than factory workers to do their modelling. In the 1870s James Hadley produced the greatest number and variety of Worcester models, including a number or Oriental subjects, Middle Eastern figures and the *Countries of the World* series. Hadley left Worcester in 1876, and in 1896 he formed his own business with his sons. Two years after his death in 1903, his business was acquired by the Worcester Royal Porcelain Company, who had also bought their last major competitor in the city, the Grainger factory, in 1889.

At this time Royal Worcester won an important battle in the courts; another Worcester firm, Locke & Co., were using the word Worcester on their pieces. The judge ruled that "Worcester" would only be used to describe products manufactured by the Worcester Royal Porcelain Company. But the Company was entering a period of crisis. From 1900 to the First World War, Worcester produced a few animal figures, often modelled by the Evans family after Japanese Netsuke

RW2609 Cow, Netsuke Animal

and Meissen style birds. During the War, the Worcester factory produced delicate porcelain figures in a style reminiscent of German crinolines, in a patriotic attempt to substitute British for German crafts. Though Frederick

M. Gertner appears to have worked on these figurines, his best and most typical work was in the highly accurate *Historical and Regimental* series, which was also introduced at this time. A number of birds and small nude figures of boys and girls also appeared at this time in Crownware. Crownware (a high-fired earthenware) was much cheaper to produce than Parian, which was phased out over this period. This proved, however, to be an unsuccessful move for the Worcester factory. Worcester tried to branch out by producing powder bowls, ashtrays and various jugs including Tobies, traditionally made by Staffordshire potters. Nothing, however, could prevent the factory from closing its doors when it went into receivership on July 24, 1930.

RW2823 Kookaburra Ashtray (Circular)

Two weeks later the factory reopened under the direction of Joseph Grimson, who wisely discontinued Crownware production. The next few years found the Worcester factory producing many new figures. Grimson and C. W. Dyson Perrins, who bought the factory, were responsible for hiring new modellers, often on a freelance basis. From then on the company saw a period to rival their heyday of the 1700s, except during the blitz and immediately after the Second World War, when production ceased almost completely. Frederick Gertner's animal brooches and menu holders, Dorothy Doughty's *American Birds*, Doris Linder's *Sporting Dogs* and *Zoo Babies* were just a few of the series produced around this time.

RW3273 Koala Bears, Billy Bluegums (with base)

Taking into account their modeller's individual preferences allowed for the development of a wide range of distinctive Worcester animal figurines. Certain

RW3269 Baltimore Oriole and Tulip Tree (Hen)

modellers are famous for the type and style of figure they chose to depict. For example, Eva Soper is well-known for her work on the *British Birds* series, while Doris

RW3813 Mallard Drake, Game Birds Series

RW4103 Robin on Holly (Style Two) "Nature Studies"

Lindner's horse and cattle models (such as the *Equestrian* series) has received wide-spread acclaim. Ronald Van Ruyckevelt created fish, flowers and birds, including the *Tropical Fish, Sporting Fish* and *Game Birds* series. Dorothy Doughty is loved worldwide for her work on *Doughty American* and *British Birds* series. James Alder was able to translate his love of birds into *British Birds (Series Two)* and *Nature Studies*, while Kenneth Potts' large size *Dogs* have received high praise.The work of these and many other modellers (including Frederick M. Gertner, Eric Aumonier, Phoebe Stabler, Stella R. Crofts, Ethelwyn Baker, E. Evans, Henri Bargas, Geraldine Blake, and many more) have created a world of animal figurines that are unique to Royal Worcester in terms of quality and tradition.

Royal Worcester has continued to expand in terms of technology and scope. Although soapstone from Cornwall in combination with the harder China Clay is the historically distinctive ingredient in Worcester ceramics, nowadays the factory makes both hard-paste ceramics with China clay, feldspar and quartz, and bone china. Bone china gets it name because it contains 50% ash from cattle bones, giving it the characteristic whiteness and translucency. Royal Worcester continues to sell dinnerware as well as figurines. In recent years the factory, under the direction of John Morris, has continued to issue quality figurines such as the ever-popular women in nineteenth and early twentieth century costume series, and series of children. Among the more prominent modellers and designers in the past years have been Kenneth and Timothy Potts, Elizabeth Greenshields (the present Design Manager) and Maureen Halson.

HOW TO COLLECT ROYAL WORCESTER ANIMALS

A collection may begin from a variety of sources. A chance gift, a souvenir picked up on holiday, or an appreciation of Royal Worcester craftsmanship can initiate a lifetime of extremely satisfying collecting. It is not unusual for very large collections to be created in a comparatively short time as one's enthusiasm rises.

For those aspiring to form a complete collection, it is advisable to keep up with all the current introductions, as they can become very elusive once discontinued. Those searching for that special piece sometimes face stiff competition, not to mention sky-high prices. Fortunately, today's collectors have a number of options when developing their collections. Auction houses and antique fairs are both excellent sources for collectors. Estate auctions are another area to explore, as are specialist dealers. The Internet can be an invaluable tool for purchasing items, as well as gathering information on a specific piece.

As accumulating every Royal Worcester animal figure produced is a rather daunting task, it is wise to decide at the beginning exactly what type of collection you wish to develop. Collections are often based around one of four general criteria: series, subject, size or artist.

Collecting by Series

Collecting by series offers the collector a general theme upon which to build a grand display of figures. *American* or *British Birds, Country Life Cameos, Dogs (small or large), Equestrian, Kittens, Prized Cattle, Sporting* or *Tropical Fish, Woodland Animals on Bronze* or *Zoo Babies* will all produce collections to be proud of. More elusive series such as the *Netsuke Animals* or *Military Commanders* will test the mettle and pocketbook of any series collector.

Collecting by Subject

Scanning through the following pages, you will find many and varied subjects around which to build a collection. A collection of bird models, for example, could include figures from the *American Birds, Birds of Prey on Bronze, British Birds, English Birds on Bronze, Nature Studies, North American Birds* and *Sporting Birds* series. As subject and series collecting have a tendency to overlap, we have provided a Collecting by Series Appendix (pages 225 to 230) to help collectors stay on course with their collections.

Collecting by Size

In today's modern world with limited space, size can be an extremely important issue. The splendour of a collection of *Military Commanders* can easily be lost if one does not have adequate space in which to display their pieces. Figurines come in all sizes, so it is easy to select complimentary pieces in a size range that will result in a handsome display.

Collecting by Artist

The work of a specific modeller such as James Alder, Stella Crofts, Dorothy or Freda Doughty, David Fryer, Frederick M. Gertner, Doris Lindner, Kenneth Potts, Raoh Schorr, Eva Soper, Ronald Van Ruyckevelt or Bernard Winskill may interest a collector.

CARE AND REPAIR

A Royal Worcester figure collection can be enjoyed indefinately as long as care is taken when handling and cleaning. When dusting, in situ, a soft cosmetic brush or photographic lens brush is useful for getting into tight corners. When necessary, glazed figures should be washed in lukewarm water, using a mild liquid detergent, then rinsed thoroughly and dried naturally or buffed gently with a soft cloth. It is important that water does not get inside the figure, so the hole in the bottom should be blocked up beforehand, perhaps with a cork or a rubber bung. Care should be taken not to knock figures against the tap or against each other as this may cause chips or imperceptible cracks in the glaze which could open up at a later date.

If the worst does happen, a professional restorer should be consulted as they can work "miracles" with damaged figures. Whether it be a small chip or a shattered body, pieces can be mended so that the repair is invisible to all but the most experienced eye. It follows that when buying figures on the secondary market, it is advisable to check for restorations. The head and any projecting pieces are the most vulnerable parts, so look at these areas carefully in a good light. Repaired cracks can be sometimes detected by looking inside the figure through the hole in the bottom. There are special ultraviolet lamps which highlight some types of restoration but these are not widely used, except by professionals. Restored figures should be priced less than perfect examples, according to the amount of damage and the quality of the repair. Always enquire about the condition of a piece when buying, as a reputable dealer will stand by any guarantees they give regarding restorations.

Insuring Your Collectables

As with any other valuables, making certain your collectables are protected is a very important concern. It is paramount that you display or store any porcelain items in a secure place, preferably one safely away from traffic in your home.

Your collectables are most often covered under your basic homeowner's policy. There are generally three kinds of such policies; standard, broad and comprehensive. Each has its own specific deductible and terms.

Under a general policy, your collectables are considered contents and are covered for all of the perils listed under the contractual terms of your policy (fire, theft, water damage and so on.)

However, since collectables are extremely delicate, breakage is treated diferently by most insurance companies. There is usually an extra premium attached to insure collectables against accidental breakage by or carelessness of the owner. This is sometimes referred to as a fine arts rider.

You are advised to contact your insurance professional to get all the answers.

In order to help protect your collection, it is critical that you take inventory of your collectables and have colour photographs taken of all your pieces. This is the surest method of establishing clearly, for the police and your insurance company, the items lost or destroyed. It is also the easiest way to establish their replacement value in the event of a tragedy.

A GUIDE TO BACKSTAMPS AND DATING

In general, mainly puce marks were used between 1900 and 1940, and from 1941 to the present black backstamps have been used exclusively. Green marks were used for the *Boer War Soldiers* series and the *First World War Soldiers*. Blue marks were used for a few series only, and red marks are known to exist.

The basic marking system, for Royal Worcester, including the crest of four linked W's surmounted by a crown, originated in 1862. From 1891, the words ROYAL WORCESTER ENGLAND appear ringed around the crest.

For every subsequent year through 1903 a dot is added near the crown, to the left side in even years, to the right in odd years. In 1904 dots are placed beneath the crest as well, one for each year until 1915.

In 1916 a star is used to replace all the dots that had accumulated, a single dot being added for each year thereafter until 1927.

Backstamps

The Puce Marks 1925-1940

	1928	Small square
	1929	Diamond
	1930	Three horizontal lines
	1931	OO (two circles)
	1932	OOO (three circles)
	1933 to 1939	Three circles and one dot Then a dot for each year

The Black Marks 1938 to date

B-1	1938	Three circles and 6 dots
	1939	Three circles and 7 dots
	1940	Three circles and 8 dots

A blue wavy line was sometimes added for 1938, 1939 and 1940

B-2	1941	Three circles and 9 dots
	1942	Three circles and 10 dots
	1943	The black mark with no date code
	1944	Bone China in large letters

	1945 to 1948	The black mark with no date code Bone China in small letters

B-3	1949	Black mark with V

B-4	1950	Black mark with W
	1951 to 1955	Black mark with W and one dot added for each year

B-5		Black mark with R inside a circle
	1956	R and 6 dots
	1957	R and 7 dots
	1958	R and 8 dots

1956 to 1972	Black mark which may or may not have dots added for years
1988	Black mark with M inside a diamond (M replaces the R)
1989	Black mark with N inside a diamond (N replaces the M)
1990 to date	Black mark with R inside a circle (Reverting back to the R inside a circle but with lithographer's numbers added to indicate the year)

ROYAL WORCESTER COLLECTORS SOCIETY

For many collectors, new series will be the most attractive option. By joining the Collectors Society, members are entitled to a free gift, the ability to purchase figurines unavailable to the general public, and a visit to the Factory, Visitor Centre and Museum. To join the Society, or get more information about Royal Worcester, contact the following:

ROYAL WORCESTER

In the United Kingdom

Royal Worcester
Severn Street, Worcester
Worcestershire WR1 2NE
Tel.: +44 (1905) 23221
Fax: +44 (1905) 23601

In the United States

The Royal China and Porcelain Companies Inc.
1265 Glen Avenue
Moorsetown, NJ 08057-0912
Tel.: (800) 257-7189

In Canada

Northdale Trading Ltd.
55-D East Beaver Creek Road
Richmond Hill
Ontario L4B 1E8
Tel.: (905) 731-9535

WHERE TO BUY

Discontinued Royal Worcester animal figures can be found in antique shops, markets, autions, shows and fairs. Specialist dealers in Royal Worcester figures attend many of these venues and events below.

For Auction happenings it is necessary to subscribe to the catalogues provided by those Auction Houses that hold 20th Century Auctions.

UNITED KINGDOM

Land-based Auction Houses

BBR Auctions
Elsecar Heritage Centre
Nr. Barnsley
South Yorkshire S74 8HJ
England
Tel.: (01226) 745156
Attn: Alan Blakeman

Bonhams
65-69 Lots Road, Chelsea
London SW10 ORN
England
Tel.: +44 (0207) 393 3900
Fax: +44 (0207) 393 3906

Christie's South Kensington
85 Old Brompton Road
London SW7 3LD
England
Tel.: +44 (0207) 581 7611
Fax: +44 (0207) 321-3321
www.christies.com
Attention: Michael Jeffrey

Potteries Specialist Auctions
271 Waterloo Road
Stoke-on-Trent ST6 3HR
Staffordshire, England
Tel.: +44 (01782) 286622
Fax: +44 (01782) 213777
Attn.: Steve Anderson

Louis Taylor
Britannia House
10 Town Road, Hanley
Stoke-on-Trent ST1 2QG, England
Tel.: +44 (01782) 214111
Fax: +44 (01782) 215283
Attn: Clive Hillier

Phillips
101 New Bond Street
London W1Y OAS, England
Tel.: +44 (0207) 629 6602
Fax: +44 (0207) 629 8876
www.phillips-auctions.com
attn: Mark Oliver

Sotheby's
34-35 New Bond Street
London W1A 2AA, England
Tel.: +44 (0207) 293 5000
Fax: +44 (0207) 293 5989

Sotheby's Sussex
Summers Place
Bilingshurst, Sussex RH1 9AF
England
Tel.: +44 (01403) 833500
Fax: +44 (01403) 833699

Thomson Roddick & Laurie
60 Whitesands
Dumfries DG1 2RS, Scotland
Tel.: +44 (01387) 255366
Fax: +44 (01387) 266236

Peter Wilson Auctioneers
Victoria Gallery, Market Street
Nantwich, Cheshire CW5 5DG
England
Tel.: +44 (01270) 623878
Fax: +44 (01270) 610508

Antique Markets

Alfie's Antique Market
13-25 Church Street
London
Tuesday - Saturday

Camden Passage Market
Islington, London N1
Wednesday and Saturday

New Caledonian Market
Bermondsey Square, London
Friday morning

Portobello Road Market
Portobello Road
London W 11
Saturday

UNITED STATES
Land-based Auction Houses

Bonhams
c/o William Doyle Galleries
175 East 87th Street
New York, NY 10128
Tel.: (212) 427-2730
Fax: (212) 369-0892

Christie's East
219 East 67th Street
New York, NY 10021
Tel.: (212) 606-040
www.christies.com
Attn: Timothy Luke

Sotheby's Arcade Auctions
1334 York Avenue
New York, NY 10021
Tel.: (212) 606-7000
www.sothebys.com
Attn: Andrew Cheney

Collectable Shows

Atlantique City
New Atlantic City Convention Center
Atlantic City, NJ
Usually March and October
For information on times and dates:
Brimfield and Associates
P.O. Box 1800, Ocean City, NJ 08226
Tel.: (609) 926-1800
www.atlantiquecity.com

O'Hare National Antiques Show & Sale
Rosemont Convention Center
Chicago, Illinois
Usually April, August and November
For information on times and dates:
Manor House Shows Inc.
P.O. Box 7320, Fort Lauderdale, FL. 33338
Tel.: (954) 563-6747

CANADA
Land-based Auction Houses

Maynards
415 West 2nd Avenue
Vancouver, BC V5Y 1E3
Tel.: (604) 876-1311

Ritchie's
288 King Street East
Toronto, Ontario M5A 1K4
Tel.: (416) 364-1864 Fax: (416) 364-0704
Attn: Caroline Kaider

Collectable Shows

Canadian Art & Collectible Show & Sale
Kitchener Memorial Auditorium
Kitchener, Ontario
Usually early May
For information on times and location:
George or Jackie Benninger
P.O. Box 130, Durham, Ontario N0G 1R0
Tel.: (519) 369-6950

Canadian Doulton & Collectible Fair
Toronto, Ontario
Usually early September
For information on times and location:
George or Jackie Benninger
P.O. Box 130, Durham, Ontario N0G 1R0
Tel.: (519) 369-6950

E-COMMERCE

Auction Sites

http://www.amazon.com/
http://www.auctions.com/
http://www.Auctions-on-line.com/
http://www.ebay.com/
http://www.auctions.excite.com/
http://www.auctions.lycos.com/
http://www.auctions.shopping.com/
http://www.auctions.xoom.com/
http://www.auctions.yahoo.com/

Antique Mall Sites

http://www.icollector.co.uk.com/
http://www.tias.com/
http://www.worldcollectorsnet.com/

The Charlton Press does not endorse any of these sites, they are listed for convenience only.

HOW TO USE THIS PRICE GUIDE

THE PURPOSE

This book is designed to serve two specific purposes. First, to furnish the Royal Worcester enthusiast with accurate listings containing vital information and photographs to aid in the building of a rewarding figure collection. Secondly, this publication provides Royal Worcester collectors and dealers with current market prices for Royal Worcester animals. Human subjects are covered in *The Charlton Standard Catalogue of Royal Worcester Figurines*, and candle extinguishers/snuffers, which may sometimes appear to be small hollow-bottomed figurines, will be treated separately in *The Charlton Standard Catalogue of Royal Worcester Collectables.*

Within the individual listings, the animals are catalogued in order of Royal Worcester (RW) model number. All listings include the modeller, height, colour, dates of issue and withdrawal, varieties and the series to which the piece belongs. Lastly, the suggested retail price is given in American, Canadian and British currencies.

VARIETY CLASSIFICATIONS

Collectors will note the following distinction concerning styles and versions:

STYLES: When two or more models have the same name but different physical modelling characteristics, they are listed as **Style One, Style Two**, and so on after their names. Such figurines will also have a different RW number.

VERSIONS: Versions are modifications to a minor style element.

VARIATIONS: Variations are modifications to a minor style element. A change in colour is a variation.

A WORD ON PRICING

In addition to providing accurate information, this catalogue gives the readers the most up-to-date retail prices for Royal Worcester animals in American, Canadian and British currencies.

To accomplish this, The Charlton Press continues to access an international pricing panel of experts who submit prices based on both dealer and collector retail-price activity, as well as current auction results in the U.S.A., Canada and the U.K. These market prices are carefully averaged to reflect accurate valuations for figures in each of these markets. All discontinued figures are priced in this manner.

Please be aware that all prices given in a particular currency are for animals within that particular country. The prices published herein have not been calculated using exchange rates exclusively. They have been determined solely by supply and demand within the country in question.

A necessary word of caution: no pricing catalogue can be, or should be, a fixed price list. This catalogue, therefore, should be considered as a pricing guide only — showing the most current retail prices based on market demand within a particular region for the various models.

Current models, however, are priced according to the manufacturer's suggested retail price. Please be aware that price or promotional sales discounting is always possible and can result in lower prices than those listed.

The prices published herein are for models in mint condition. Collectors are cautioned that a repaired or restored piece may be worth as little as 25 per cent of the value of the same model in mint condition. The collector interested strictly in investment potential will avoid damaged models.

THE INTERNET AND PRICING

Over three years ago we wrote a column for the introduction of our guides dealing with the Internet and the impact it would have on the collecting industry. In this column we gave the reasons why the Internet would affect collectables and their selling price, and also how it would impact and change the way collectors acquire items for their collections.

All this is certainly happening. The industry is now in the sea of change. On the World Wide Web it makes no difference what you collect - coins, stamps, ceramics, art pottery, glass, books - all and sundry are impacted. Naturally, the Van Gogh's are not, but leaving out the high priced items or the exotics, all collectables are and will be affected.

The Web has lowered the transaction cost between the buyer and the seller to a point where land-based sellers (dealers, auction houses) cannot compete under the old rules.

Collectables and collections used to flow through the old supply chain: estate or non-collector/picker/dealer/collector/land auction/dealer/collector. Naturally, the chain could be interrupted or jumped when convenient.

The new chain which moves items at a much faster rate, and at a much lower cost, maybe outlined as follows: estate, non-collector, picker, collector, dealer/on-line auction/dealer/collector.

Retail stores and malls have closed. Collectable/Antique Fairs and Shows are losing dealers simply because collectors are changing their buying habits. Collectable Shows are too long and too drawn out. High-end Antique/Decorator Shows still can support long openings, for besides being fairs, they are a form of entertainment.

The following is a chart of the number of items, by type, that appear on a major on-line auction site:

Category	Items Daily	Items Projected To Yearly Basis
Coins	6,000	2,190,000
Disney	37,500	13,687,500
Harry Potter	2,300	839,500
Lalique	650	237,250
Moorcroft	250	91,250
Royal Doulton	3,500	1,277,500
Royal Worcester	600	219,000
Stamps	12,750	4,654,000
Star Wars	19,000	6,935,000

As you can see, the numbers are staggering. This major site advertises "over 5 million items for sale." That is over 1.8 billion items yearly.

Of course, these are not all collectables but one can become easily dismayed by such numbers. Turning to a positive point of view, it also signifies tremendous interest and awareness in things collectable. This major on-line auction has sites in Australia, Austria, Canada, France, Germany, Italy, Japan, the United Kingdon and the United States. Three years ago it was only the United States. What happens now, will the rest of the world (China, India) join in? When they do, the interest and awareness will only continue to build.

Certainly, collecting is a function of disposable income, but that is also improving worldwide. What is happening to prices? We, Charlton, come from a numismatic background, based in the 1960s, 70s and 80s. Our experience derives from a market that has seen wild gyrations in the supply and demand for over a forty-year period. Equating the numismatic market to the collectable market, what appears to be happening in the collectable field is exactly what occurred in the great coin melts of the late sixties to early eighties. The flood gates opened - attics, basements, garages, storage rooms, grandma's and grandpa's houses all disgorged their (coins) goodies. Today's collectables are being rushed to an on-line auction site (the melting pot), where they may be disposed of regardless of price.

How long will this go on? In the coin market, the melts lasted (as long as the precious metal prices rose) nearly 20 years. The rise in the intrinsic value of coins drew all and sundry out onto the market, identical to what is now happening to the on-line auctions and all collectables.

Everyone is rushing, looking for the next item to list on the on-line auction. When some item makes a tremendous splash (at a very high price), the hunt is on to find another like it.

With supply rising, prices will fall. Competition in the early stages will not be demand driven, but supply driven. With more competition, prices will fall. So what's the forecast?

Now, remember, this is over a long time period. Prices will move down from highs of the late-nineties, into lows for the mid-2000, and then rise again in mid-2010. The time frame mentioned may be over-estimated for we do deal with an infinite supply and the rate at which items change hands is certainly rapid.

Our guide prices will, over time, have the look of a large saucer-shaped curve for prices will rise.

Now this will not apply across the board, for what is now scarce will probably remain scarce. However, some will turn from scarce to plentiful as the flood changes the supply. The reverse will also be true, some things that are thought to be plentiful will be found to be scarce. There is one certainty: it will be an interesting time.

FURTHER READING

The Charlton Standard Catalogue of Royal Worcester Figurines,
by Anthony Cast and John Edwards
The Charlton Price Guide to Royal Worcester Figurines: Models by Freda Doughty,
by Anthony Cast and John Edwards
The Collectors Handbook of Marks and Monograms on Pottery and Porcelain,
by William Chaffers (revised by Referick Litchfield)
The Country Life Collector's Pocket Book of China, by G. Bernard Hughes
Encyclopaedia of British Pottery and Porcelain Marks, by Geoffrey A. Godden
English Ceramics: The Frances & Emory Cocke Collection, by Donald C. Peirce
English Pottery and Porcelain, by W. B. Honey
A Guide to the Dating of Royal Worcester Porcelain Marks from 1862, by Derek Shirley
An Illustrated Encyclopaedia of British Pottery and Porcelain, by Geoffrey A. Godden
The Parian Phenomenon, by Paul Atterbury
A Picture Book of Royal Worcester Figurines, by H. E. Frost
Royal Worcester Porcelain and the Dyson Perrins Collection,
by Harry Frost and Wendy Cook
The Sandon Guide to Royal Worcester Figurines 1900-1970,
by David, John and Henry Sandon
Wigornia News (periodical)

ROYAL WORCESTER ANIMALS 1900 to date

RW2894 Boy with Donkey

RW2400
COCKEREL STRING BOX

Modeller: Unknown
Height: Unknown
Colour: Unknown
Issued: 1905

Colourways	*Backstamp*	*U.S. $*	*Price* *Can. $*	*U.K. £*
Unknown	Puce		Rare	

Photograph not available at press time

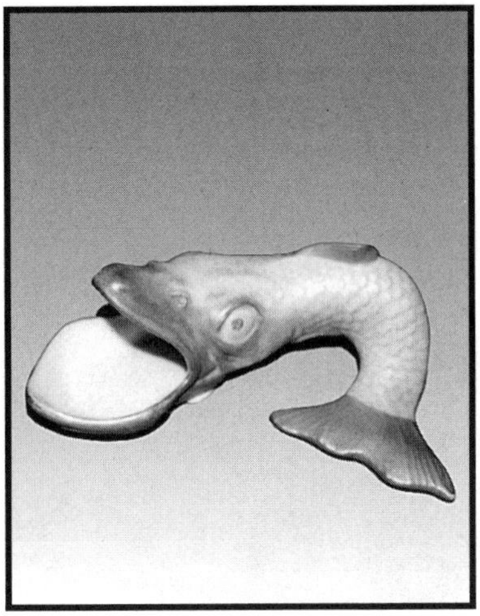

RW2484
FISH ASHTRAY

Modeller: Unknown
Height: 5″, 12.7 cm
Colour: 1. Blue
2. Green
3. Light orange
4. White
Issued: 1909

Colourways	*Backstamp*	*U.S. $*	*Price* *Can. $*	*U.K. £*
1. Coloured (as above)	Puce	225.00	300.00	150.00
2. White	Green	175.00	250.00	125.00

RW2514
BRER RABBIT FLOWER HOLDER

Modeller: Unknown
Height: 4 ¾″, 12.1 cm
Colour: 1. New silks
2. White
Issued: 1911

Colourways	*Backstamp*	*U.S. $*	*Price* *Can. $*	*U.K. £*
1. Coloured (as above)	Puce	425.00	600.00	300.00
2. White	Green	275.00	400.00	200.00

RW2517
DUCK RING STAND

Modeller: Unknown
Height: 6 ½″, 16.5 cm
Colour: Unknown
Issued: 1911-by 1927

Colourways	*Backstamp*	*U.S. $*	*Price* *Can. $*	*U.K. £*
Unknown	Puce	500.00	700.00	350.00

RW2537
PEACOCK MENU HOLDER

Modeller: Unknown
Height: 3 ¼″, 8.3 cm
Colour: Unknown
Issued: 1912

Colourways	*Backstamp*	*U.S. $*	*Price* *Can. $*	*U.K. £*
Unknown	Puce	250.00	350.00	175.00

RW2604
TORTOISE

Modeller: Unknown
Size: 1 ¼″ x 4 ½″, 3.2 x 11.9 cm
Colour: 1. White with tinted head, tail and feet
2. Shot colours
Issued: 1916-c.1950s
Series: Netsuke Animals

Colourways	*Backstamp*	*U.S. $*	*Price* *Can. $*	*U.K. £*
Coloured (as above)	Green	900.00	1,250.00	650.00

RW2605
SNAIL
Style One

Modeller: Unknown
Height: 1″, 2.5 cm
Length: 1 ¾″, 4.4 cm
Colour: 1. Blush ivory
2. Shot colours
3. Strong enamel colours
4. White with tinted features
Issued: 1916-c.1950s
Series: Netsuke Animals

Colourways	*Backstamp*	*U.S. $*	*Price* *Can. $*	*U.K. £*
Coloured (as above)	Green	400.00	550.00	275.00

RW2606
CHEETAH

Modeller: Unknown
Length: 3 ¼″, 8.3 cm
Colour: 1. Blush ivory
2. Cream with light brown, pink and grey highlights
3. Dark blue
Issued: 1916-c.1950s
Series: Netsuke Animals

Colourways	*Backstamp*	*U.S. $*	*Price* *Can. $*	*U.K. £*
Coloured (as above)	Green	550.00	800.00	400.00

RW2607
RABBIT

Modeller: Unknown
Height: 1″, 2.5 cm
Length: 2″, 5.0 cm
Colour: 1. Natural colours
2. Strong enamel colours
3. White with pink eyes
4. White with tinted body
Issued: 1916-by 1960
Series: Netsuke Animals

Colourways	*Backstamp*	*U.S. $*	*Price* *Can. $*	*U.K. £*
Coloured (as above)	Green	225.00	300.00	150.00

Note: This model was also produced as a menu holder, with a slit cut into the back.

RW2608
SNAKE

Modeller: Unknown
Height: 1", 2.5 cm
Length: 4", 10.1 cm
Colour: 1. Shot colours
2. White
Issued: 1916-c.1975
Series: Netsuke Animals

			Price	
Description	***Backstamp***	***U.S. $***	***Can. $***	***U.K. £***
1. Original issue	Green	1,500.00	2,000.00	1,000.00
2. Reissued	Black	350.00	500.00	250.00

RW2609
COW

Modeller: Unknown
Length: 6", 15.0 cm
Colour: 1. Black enamel
2. Strong colours
Issued: 1916-c.1950s
Series: Netsuke Animals

			Price	
Colourways	***Backstamp***	***U.S. $***	***Can. $***	***U.K. £***
Coloured (as above)	Green	1,500.00	2,000.00	1,000.00

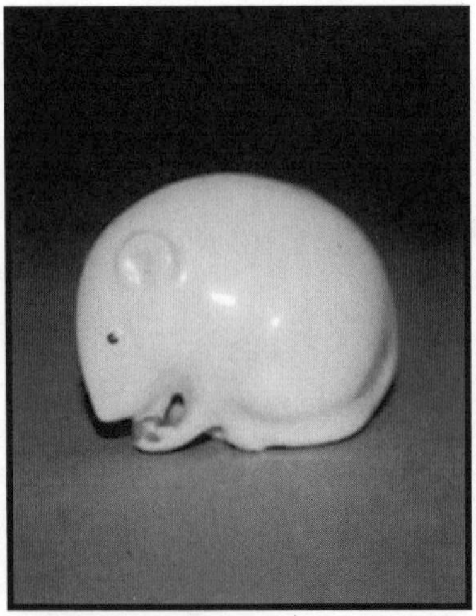

RW2610
MOUSE

Modeller: Unknown
Height: 1", 2.5 cm
Length: 2", 5.0 cm
Colour: 1. Natural colours
2. Strong colours
3. White with pink eyes
4. White with tinted body
Issued: 1916-by 1960
Varieties: Mouse Ashtray (Right) RW2827; Mouse Ashtray (Left) RW2828
Series: Netsuke Animals

			Price	
Colourways	***Backstamp***	***U.S. $***	***Can. $***	***U.K. £***
Coloured (as above)	Green	175.00	250.00	125.00

RW2611
FISH

Modeller:	Unknown
Height:	1", 2.5 cm
Length:	4", 10.1 cm
Colour:	1. Blush ivory
	2. Tinted
	3. White
Issued:	1916-c.1950s
Series:	Netsuke Animals

Colourways	*Backstamp*	*U.S. $*	*Price* *Can. $*	*U.K. £*
Coloured (as above)	Green	400.00	550.00	275.00

RW2612
APE

Modeller:	Unknown
Height:	2 ¾", 7.0 cm
Colour:	1. Blush ivory
	2. Bright enamel colours
	3. Tinted
Issued:	1916-c.1950s
Series:	Netsuke Animals

Colourways	*Backstamp*	*U.S. $*	*Price* *Can. $*	*U.K. £*
Coloured (as above)	Green	350.00	500.00	250.00

RW2613
RAM

Modeller:	Unknown
Length:	2 ¼", 5.7 cm
Colour:	1. Bright colours
	2. Ivory
	3. White with light grey shading
Issued:	1916-c.1950s
Series:	Netsuke Animals

Colourways	*Backstamp*	*U.S. $*	*Price* *Can. $*	*U.K. £*
Coloured (as above)	Green	400.00	550.00	275.00

RW2622
BLACKCOCK

Modeller: Unknown
Height: 3", 7.6 cm
Colour: 1. Black
2. White with grey and light green highlights
Issued: 1916-c.1950s
Series: Netsuke Animals

Colourways	*Backstamp*	*U.S. $*	*Price Can. $*	*U.K. £*
Coloured (as above)	Green	500.00	700.00	350.00

RW2623
QUAIL

Modeller: Unknown
Height: 2", 5.1 cm
Colour: Bright colours
Issued: 1916-c.1950s
Series: Netsuke Animals

Colourways	*Backstamp*	*U.S. $*	*Price Can. $*	*U.K. £*
Bright colours	Green	425.00	600.00	300.00

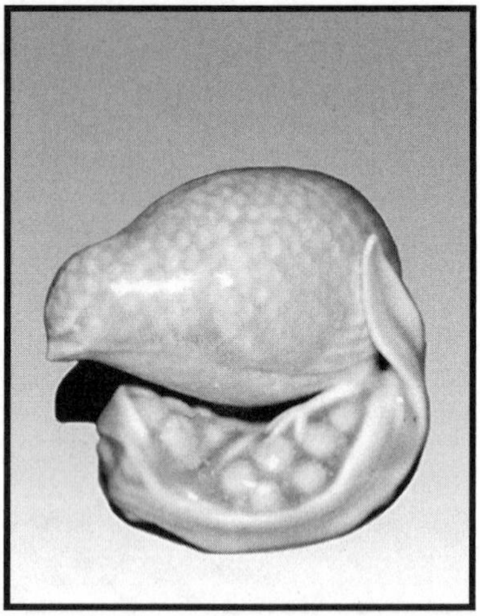

RW2624
TOAD

Modeller: Unknown
Height: 1 ¾", 4.5 cm
Colour: 1. Blush ivory
2. Bright enamels
3. Shot bronze (matte)
4. White with tinted features
Issued: 1916-c1950s
Series: Netsuke Animals

Colourways	*Backstamp*	*U.S. $*	*Price Can. $*	*U.K. £*
Coloured (as above)	Green	425.00	600.00	300.00

RW2636
DOUBLE MOUSE

Modeller:	Unknown
Height:	2 ½", 6.4 cm
Colour:	1. Shot bronze and ivory 2. White with tinted features
Issued:	1916
Series:	Netsuke Animals

Colourways	*Backstamp*	*U.S. $*	*Price* *Can. $*	*U.K. £*
Coloured (as above)	Green	625.00	900.00	450.00

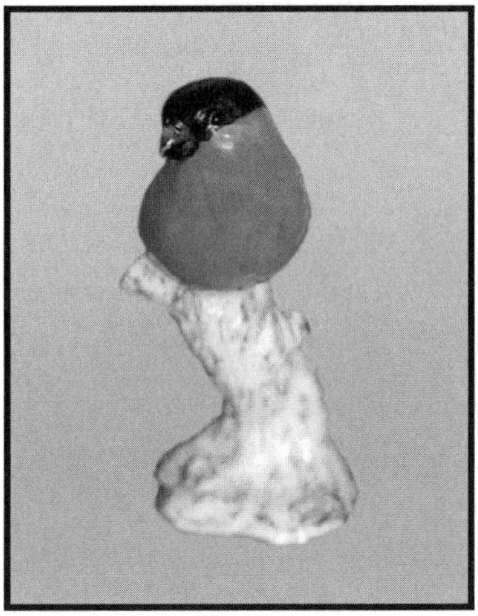

RW2662
BULLFINCH (On stump)

Modeller:	Frederick M. Gertner
Height:	6", 15.0 cm
Colour:	Red-brown breast, blue-grey feathers; white stump with gilt flecks and painted flowers
Issued:	Crownware: 1. 1917 Bone china: 2. 1918-1977
Series:	Birds on Stumps

Description	*Backstamp*	*U.S. $*	*Price* *Can. $*	*U.K. £*
1. Crownware	Puce	250.00	350.00	175.00
2. Bone china	Puce	325.00	450.00	225.00
3. Bone china	Black	250.00	350.00	175.00

Note: RW2662-2667 were also issued as Flower Holders / Table Decorations with holes in the stumps.

RW2663
PARROQUET, Female (On stump)
Style One

Modeller:	Frederick M. Gertner
Height:	7", 17.8 cm
Colour:	1. Blue bird with black markings; white stump with gilt flecks and painted flowers 2. Green bird with black markings; white stump with gilt flecks and painted flowers 3. Yellow bird; white stump with gilt flecks and painted flowers
Issued:	1. Crownware: 1917 2. Bone china: 1918-1977
Series:	Birds on Stumps

Description	*Backstamp*	*U.S. $*	*Price* *Can. $*	*U.K. £*
1. Crownware	Puce	200.00	300.00	150.00
2. Bone china	Puce	325.00	450.00	225.00
3. Bone china	Black	265.00	375.00	190.00

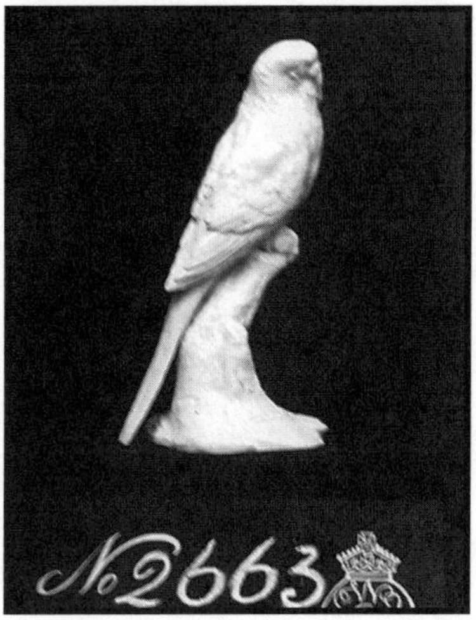

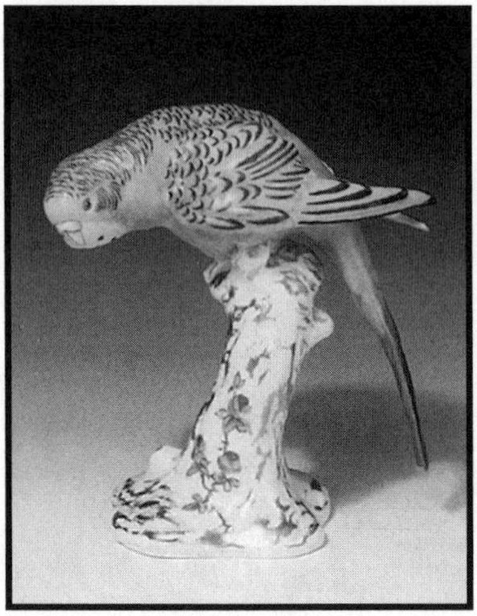

RW2664
PARROT, Male (On stump)

Modeller: Frederick M. Gertner
Height: 5", 12.7 cm
Colour: 1. Blue bird with black markings; white stump with gilt flecks and painted flowers
2 Green bird with black and yellow markings; white stump with gilt flecks and painted flowers
3. Yellow bird with black markings; white stump with gilt flecks and painted flowers
Issued: 1. Crownware: 1917
2. Bone china: 1918-1977
Varieties: Also called "Parroquet," Style Two
Series: Birds on Stumps

			Price	
Description	*Backstamp*	*U.S. $*	*Can. $*	*U.K. £*
1. Crownware	Puce	250.00	350.00	180.00
2. Bone china	Puce	360.00	525.00	260.00
3. Bone china	Black	300.00	450.00	220.00

RW2665
CANARY (On stump)

Modeller: Frederick M. Gertner
Height: 6 ¼", 15.9 cm
Colour: Bright yellow bird; white stump with gilt flecks and painted flowers
Issued: Crownware:
1. 1917
Bone china:
2. 1918-1977
Series: Birds on Stumps

			Price	
Description	*Backstamp*	*U.S. $*	*Can. $*	*U.K. £*
1. Crownware	Puce	200.00	300.00	150.00
2. Bone china	Puce	275.00	400.00	200.00
3. Bone china	Black	250.00	350.00	175.00

RW2666
KINGFISHER (On stump)

Modeller: Frederick M. Gertner
Height: 5 ¾", 14.6 cm
Colour: Orangey-red breast, blue flowers; white stump with gilt flecks and painted flowers
Issued: Crownware:
1. 1917
Bone china
2. 1918-1977
Series: Birds on Stumps

			Price	
Description	*Backstamp*	*U.S. $*	*Can. $*	*U.K. £*
1. Crownware	Puce	225.00	325.00	160.00
2. Bone china	Puce	275.00	400.00	200.00
3. Bone china	Black	250.00	350.00	175.00

RW2667
GOLDFINCH (On stump)

Modeller: Frederick M. Gertner
Height: 5 ¾″, 14.6 cm
Colour: 1. Red head, yellow breast; green-brown base (Crownware)
2. Red head, red-brown breast; white stump with gilt flecks and painted flowers (Bone china)
Issued: Crownware:
1. 1917
Bone china:
2. 1918-1977
Series: Birds on Stumps

Description	Backstamp	U.S. $	Price Can. $	U.K. £
1. Crownware	Puce	225.00	325.00	150.00
2. Bone china	Puce	275.00	400.00	200.00
3. Bone china	Black	250.00	350.00	175.00

RW2695
FLAMINGO (Neck curved)

Modeller: Frederick M. Gertner
Height: 6″, 15.0 cm (mounted on brass legs)
Colour: Pink
Issued: 1918

Colourways	Backstamp	U.S. $	Price Can. $	U.K. £
Pink	Puce	375.00	550.00	275.00

Note: This bird was intended to be mounted on brass legs.

RW2696
FLAMINGO (Neck stretched forward)

Modeller: Frederick M. Gertner
Height: 6″, 15.0 cm (mounted on brass legs)
Colour: Pink
Issued: 1918

Colourways	Backstamp	U.S. $	Price Can. $	U.K. £
Pink	Puce	375.00	550.00	275.00

Note: This bird was intended to be mounted on brass legs.

RW2780A
TIGER (Lying, facing left)

Modeller: Frederick M. Gertner
Height: 3", 7.6 cm
Colour: 1. Golden brown with dark brown stripes
2. White
Issued: 1920-by 1940

Colourways	*Backstamp*	*U.S. $*	*Price* *Can. $*	*U.K. £*
1. Coloured (as above)	Puce	1,200.00	1,600.00	800.00
2. White	Green	550.00	800.00	400.00

RW2780B
TIGER (Lying, facing right)

Modeller: Frederick M. Gertner
Height: 3", 7.6 cm
Colour: 1. Golden brown with dark brown stripes
2. White
Issued: 1920-by 1940

Colourways	*Backstamp*	*U.S. $*	*Price* *Can. $*	*U.K. £*
1. Coloured (as above)	Puce	1,200.00	1,600.00	800.00
2. White	Green	550.00	800.00	400.00

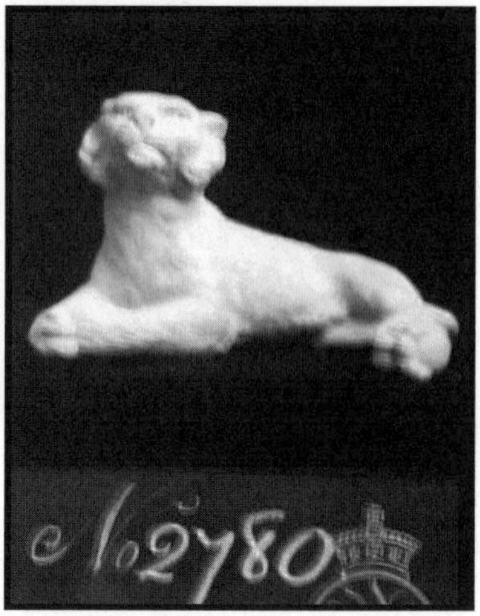

RW2821A
KOOKABURRA

Modeller: Frederick M. Gertner
Height: 2 ¼", 5.7 cm
Colour: 1. Yellow, white and grey
2. White
Issued: c. 1923-by 1927
Varieties: Kookaburra Ashtray (Circular) RW2823;
Kookaburra Ashtray (Rectangular) RW2822;
Kookaburra Powder Bowl RW2821B

Colourways	*Backstamp*	*U.S. $*	*Price* *Can. $*	*U.K. £*
1. Coloured (as above)	Puce		Very rare	
2. White	Green		Very rare	

Note: Although the Kookaburra was issued as a separate model, it was only given a model number when used as a derivative.

RW2821B
KOOKABURRA POWDER BOWL

Modeller: Frederick M. Gertner
Size: 4 ¾" x 6", 12.1 x 15.0 cm
Colour: Yellow, white and grey bird; powder blue and gold bowl
Issued: 1923
Varieties: Kookaburra RW2821A;
Kookaburra Ashtray (Circular) RW2823;
Kookaburra Ashtray (Rectangular) RW2822

			Price	
Colourways	*Backstamp*	*U.S. $*	*Can. $*	*U.K. £*
Coloured (as above)	Puce	375.00	550.00	275.00

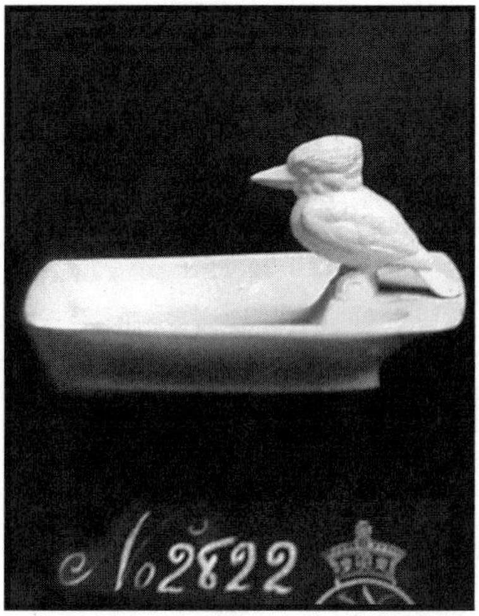

RW2822
KOOKABURRA ASHTRAY (Rectangular)

Modeller: Frederick M. Gertner
Size: 2 ¼" x 4" x 5 ½", 5.7 x 10.1 x 14.0 cm
Colour: 1. Yellow, white and grey bird; gold edged tray
2. Yellow, white and grey bird; powder blue tray
3. White
Issued: 1924
Varieties: Kookaburra RW2821A;
Kookaburra Ashtray (Circular) RW2823;
Kookaburra Powder Bowl RW2821B

			Price	
Colourways	*Backstamp*	*U.S. $*	*Can. $*	*U.K. £*
1. Coloured (as above)	Puce	350.00	500.00	250.00
2. White	Green	200.00	300.00	150.00

RW2823
KOOKABURRA ASHTRAY (Circular)

Modeller: Frederick M. Gertner
Height: 2 ¼", 5.7 cm
Colour: 1. Yellow, white and grey bird; black tray
2. Yellow, white and grey bird; powder blue tray
3. White
Issued: 1924
Varieties: Kookaburra RW2821A;
Kookaburra Ashtray (Rectangular) RW2822;
Kookaburra Powder Bowl RW2821B

			Price	
Colourways	*Backstamp*	*U.S. $*	*Can. $*	*U.K. £*
1. Coloured (as above)	Puce	350.00	500.00	250.00
2. White	Green	200.00	300.00	150.00

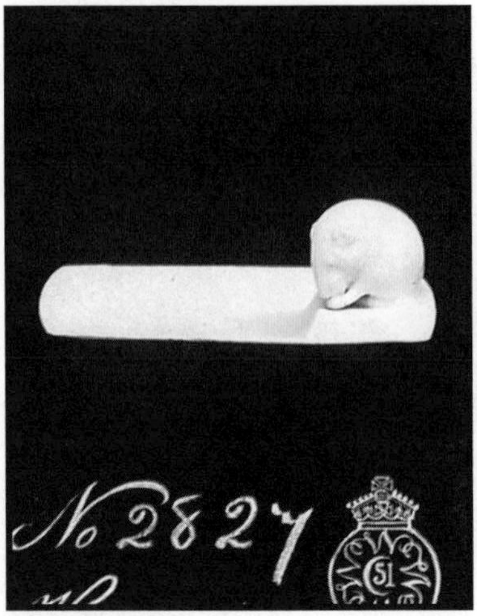

RW2827
MOUSE ASHTRAY (Right)

Modeller: Unknown
Size: 5 ½" x 4 ¼" x 2", 14.0 x 10.8 x 5.0 cm
Colour: 1. Tinted mouse; powder blue tray
2. White
Issued: 1924-by 1953
Varieties: Mouse RW2610; Mouse Ashtray (Left) RW2828

Colourways	*Backstamp*	*U.S. $*	*Price Can. $*	*U.K. £*
1. Coloured (as above)	Puce	185.00	250.00	125.00
2. Coloured (as bove)	Black	150.00	200.00	100.00
3. White	Green	150.00	200.00	100.00

RW2828
MOUSE ASHTRAY (Left)

Modeller: Unknown
Size: 5 ½" x 4 ¼" x 2", 14.0 x 10.8 x 5.0 cm
Colour: 1. Tinted mouse; powder blue tray
2. White
Issued: 1924-by 1953
Varieties: Mouse RW2610; Mouse Ashtray (Right) RW2827

Colourways	*Backstamp*	*U.S. $*	*Price Can. $*	*U.K. £*
1. Coloured (as above)	Puce	185.00	250.00	125.00
2. Coloured (as above)	Black	150.00	200.00	100.00
3. White	Green	150.00	200.00	100.00

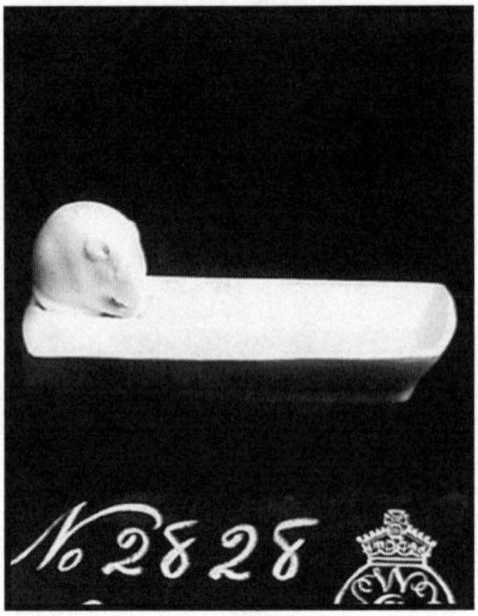

RW2842
WILFRED

Modeller: Frederick M. Gertner
Height: 4 ¾", 12.1 cm
Colour: 1. Brown and white body; pink nose; black base
2. White
Issued: 1927-by 1930

Colourways	*Backstamp*	*U.S. $*	*Price Can. $*	*U.K. £*
1. Coloured (as above)	Puce	350.00	500.00	250.00
2. White	Green	225.00	300.00	150.00

RW2843
DUCK

Modeller: Frederick M. Gertner
Height: 3 ¾", 9.5 cm
Colour: 1. Yellow body; orange feet and beak; green base
2. White
Issued: 1927-by 1930

Colourways	*Backstamp*	*U.S. $*	*Price Can. $*	*U.K. £*
1. Coloured (as above)	Puce	500.00	700.00	350.00
2. White	Green	350.00	500.00	250.00

RW2851A
ELEPHANT JUG

Modeller: Frederick M. Gertner
Height: 3 ½", 8.9 cm
Colour: 1. Grey elephant; orange handle; black base
2. White
Issued: 1929

Colourways	*Backstamp*	*U.S. $*	*Price Can. $*	*U.K. £*
1. Coloured (as above)	Puce	425.00	600.00	300.00
2. White	Green	275.00	400.00	200.00

RW2851B
ELEPHANT SALT, PEPPER AND MUSTARD POTS

Modeller: Frederick M. Gertner
Height: 3 ½", 8.9 cm
Colour: 1. Mustard Pot: Unknown
2. Pepper: Black elephant; orange top and base
3. Salt: Grey elephant; orange top; black base
4. White
Issued: 1929

Description	*Backstamp*	*U.S. $*	*Price Can. $*	*U.K. £*
1. Mustard pot	Puce	350.00	500.00	250.00
2. Pepper	Puce	350.00	500.00	250.00
3. Salt	Puce	350.00	500.00	250.00
4. Cruet set (coloured)	Puce	1,000.00	1,500.00	750.00
5. Cruet set (white)	Green	700.00	1,000.00	500.00

Note: Rims are E.P.N.S.

RW2852A
COCKATOO JUG

Modeller: Frederick M. Gertner
Height: 3 ¼", 8.3 cm
Colour: 1. Coloured
2. White
Issued: 1929

Colourways	*Backstamp*	*U.S. $*	*Price Can. $*	*U.K. £*
1. Coloured	Puce	425.00	600.00	300.00
2. White	Green	275.00	400.00	200.00

RW2852B
COCKATOO SALT AND PEPPER POTS

Modeller: Frederick M. Gertner
Height: 3 ¼", 8.3 cm
Colour: Unknown
Issued: 1929

Description	*Backstamp*	*U.S. $*	*Price Can. $*	*U.K. £*
1. Pepper	Puce		Very rare,	
2. Salt	Puce		few made	

Photograph not available at press time

Note: Rims are E.P.N.S.

RW2853A
PELICAN JUG

Modeller: Frederick M. Gertner
Height: 4 ¼", 10.8 cm
Colour: 1. Light grey, white and black body; yellow beak; green handle
2. White
Issued: 1929 by 1940

Colourways	*Backstamp*	*U.S. $*	*Price Can. $*	*U.K. £*
1. Coloured (as above)	Puce	425.00	600.00	300.00
2. White	Green	275.00	400.00	200.00

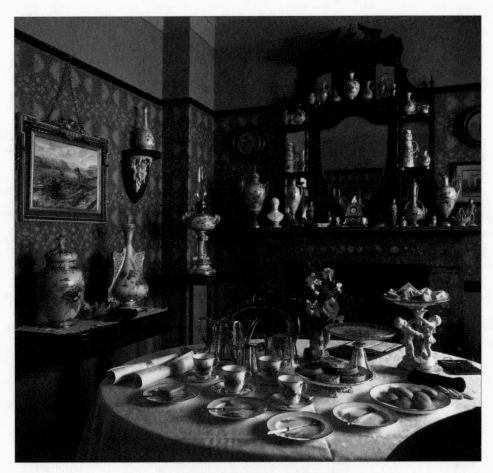

RW2853B
PELICAN SALT AND PEPPER POTS

Modeller: Frederick M. Gertner
Height: 4 ¼", 10.8 cm
Colour: 1. Light grey, white and black body; yellow beak; green base
2. White
Issued: 1929-by 1940

			Price	
Colourways	*Backstamp*	*U.S. $*	*Can. $*	*U.K. £*
1. Coloured (as above)	Puce	350.00	500.00	250.00
2. White	Green	225.00	300.00	150.00

RW2854A
SQUIRREL JUG

Modeller: Frederick M. Gertner
Height: 3 ¼", 8.3 cm
Colour: 1. Brown squirrel; green leaf spout
2. White
Issued: 1929

			Price	
Colourways	*Backstamp*	*U.S. $*	*Can. $*	*U.K. £*
1. Coloured (as above)	Puce	425.00	600.00	300.00
2. White	Green	275.00	400.00	200.00

RW2854B
SQUIRREL SALT AND PEPPER POTS

Modeller: Frederick M. Gertner
Height: 3 ¼", 8.3 cm
Colour: 1. Brown squirrel; green base and lid
2. White
Issued: 1929

			Price	
Colourways	*Backstamp*	*U.S. $*	*Can. $*	*U.K. £*
1. Coloured (as above)	Puce	350.00	500.00	250.00
2. White	Green	225.00	300.00	150.00

Photograph not available at press time

RW2855A
BONZO

Modeller: Frederick M. Gertner
Height: 3″, 7.6 cm
Colour: 1. Black with tinting
2. Fawn and black
3. Puce and pink
4. Tinted white with black patches; black collar; pink tongue
Issued: 1929
Varieties: Bonzo Salt and Pepper Pots RW2855B

Colourways	*Backstamp*	*U.S. $*	*Price Can. $*	*U.K. £*
Coloured (as above)	Puce	550.00	800.00	400.00

RW2855B
BONZO SALT AND PEPPER POTS

Modeller: Frederick M. Gertner
Height: 3 ¼″, 8.3 cm
Colour: 1. Black with tinting
2. Fawn and black
3. Puce and pink
4. Tinted white with black patches; black collar; pink tongue
Issued: 1929
Varieties: Bonzo RW2855A

Description	*Backstamp*	*U.S. $*	*Price Can. $*	*U.K. £*
1. Pepper	Puce	500.00	700.00	350.00
2. Salt	Puce	500.00	700.00	350.00

Note: The top of the head of the original Bonzo figure was pierced to create salt and pepper pots.

RW2858A
BRER RABBIT

Modeller: Frederick M. Gertner
Height: 3 ¼″, 8.3 cm
Colour: 1. Blue coat; red waistcoat
2. Green coat; red waistcoat
3. Red coat; blue waistcoat
Issued: 1929-by 1940
Varieties: Brer Rabbit Salt and Pepper Pots RW2858B

Colourways	*Backstamp*	*U.S. $*	*Price Can. $*	*U.K. £*
Coloured (as above)	Puce	500.00	700.00	350.00

RW2858B
BRER RABBIT SALT AND PEPPER POTS

Modeller: Frederick M. Gertner
Height: 3 ¼", 8.3 cm
Colour: Unknown
Issued: 1929
Varieties: Brer Rabbit RW2858A

Description	*Backstamp*	*U.S. $*	*Price Can. $*	*U.K. £*
1. Pepper	Puce		Very rare,	
2. Salt	Puce		few made	

Photograph not available at press time

RW2870
TERRIER (On plinth)

Modeller: Doris Lindner
Height: 3 ½", 8.9 cm
Colour: 1. White with red brown patches; fawn base
2. White with grey patches; green base
Issued: 1931-by 1940
Varieties: Terrier Powder Bowl / Bon Bon Box RW2927; Wire-Haired Terrier (Standing, head to right, without plinth) RW3026

Description	*Backstamp*	*U.S. $*	*Price Can. $*	*U.K. £*
Coloured (as above)	Puce	325.00	450.00	225.00

RW2871
SETTER (On plinth)

Modeller: Doris Lindner
Height: 3", 7.6 cm
Colour: 1. Chestnut red; fawn base
2. Chestnut red; green base
Issued: 1931-by 1953
Varieties: Setter (Without plinth) RW2952

Backstamp	*U.S. $*	*Price Can. $*	*U.K. £*
1. Puce	400.00	475.00	225.00
2. Black	350.00	400.00	175.00

RW2872
HOUND ASHTRAY

Modeller: Doris Lindner
Size: 2" x 4", 5.1 x 10.1 cm
Colour: White with chestnut brown and black spots; cream tray
Issued: 1931-by c.1960s
Varieties: Hound (Lying on curved base) RW2951;
Hound Tobacco Jar RW2926

	Price		
Backstamp	*U.S. $*	*Can. $*	*U.K. £*
1. Puce	175.00	250.00	125.00
2. Black	135.00	200.00	95.00

Note: Produced for Betzemann.

RW2873
FOX ASHTRAY

Modeller: Doris Lindner
Size: 2" x 4", 5.1 x 10.1 cm
Colour: Chestnut red fox; cream tray
Issued: 1931-by c.1960s
Varieties: Fox (Lying, on curved base) RW2950;
Fox (Lying, without base)RW3527;
Fox Tobacco Jar RW2925

	Price		
Backstamp	*U.S. $*	*Can. $*	*U.K. £*
1. Puce	175.00	250.00	125.00
2. Black	135.00	200.00	95.00

Note: Produced for Betzemann.

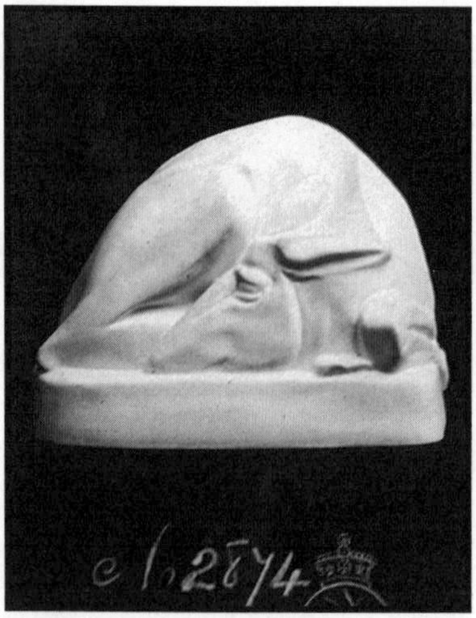

RW2874
SLEEPING DOE

Modeller: Eric Aumonier
Height: 4 ¾", 12.1 cm
Colour: 1. Buff and maroon
2. Mottled grey
Issued: 1931

			Price	
Colourways	*Backstamp*	*U.S. $*	*Can. $*	*U.K. £*
Coloured (as above)	Puce	550.00	800.00	400.00

RW2875
HORSEMAN BOOKEND

Modeller: Eric Aumonier
Height: 8 ¼", 21.0 cm
Colour: Horseman: Green trousers, hat, collar
Horse: White; blue tassles; gold circles; blue, gold and black on hooves
Issued: 1931-by 1940

Colourways	*Backstamp*	*U.S. $*	*Price Can. $*	*U.K. £*
Green/white/blue/gold/black	Puce	425.00	600.00	300.00

Note: Available with or without the wooden fitting.

RW2876
LION BOOKEND

Modeller: Eric Aumonier
Height: 8 ¼", 21.0 cm
Colour: Mottled grey with green circles; blue claws
Issued: 1931-by 1940

Colourways	*Backstamp*	*U.S. $*	*Price Can. $*	*U.K. £*
Mottled grey	Puce	425.00	600.00	300.00

Note: Available with or without the wooden fitting.

RW2877A
YOUNG HORSE

Modeller: Eric Aumonier
Height: 1. With base: 6 ¼", 15.9 cm
2. Without base: 6", 15.0 cm
Colour: 1. Mottled grey with or without base
2. Pinky beige with or without base
Issued: 1931-by 1940
Varieties: Young Horse Ink Blotter RW2877B

Description	*Backstamp*	*U.S. $*	*Price Can. $*	*U.K. £*
1. With base	Puce	275.00	400.00	200.00
2. Without base	Puce	275.00	400.00	200.00

Note: Produced for Betzemann for mounting.

RW2877B
YOUNG HORSE INK BLOTTER

Modeller: Eric Aumonier
Width: 7", 17.8 cm
Colour: White horse; mirror base; black blotter
Issued: 1931-by 1940
Varieties: Young Horse RW2877A

Colourways	*Backstamp*	*Price* *U.S. $*	*Can. $*	*U.K. £*
Coloured (as above)	Puce	350.00	500.00	250.00

Note: Produced for Betzemann for mounting.

RW2882
BOY ON BOAR

Modeller: Phoebe Stabler
Height: 3 ½", 8.9 cm
Colour: Fleshtone; blonde hair; shaded brown pig; pale green oval base
Issued: 1931-by 1940

Colourways	*Backstamp*	*Price* *U.S. $*	*Can. $*	*U.K. £*
Fleshtone/brown/green	Puce	1,300.00	1,600.00	650.00

RW2891
GREYHOUNDS

Modeller: Stella R. Crofts
Size: 3" x 6 ¾", 7.6 x 17.2 cm
Colour: Brown; white with black patches; black; white with black patches; beige base
Issued: 1931

Colourways	*Backstamp*	*Price* *U.S. $*	*Can. $*	*U.K. £*
Brown/black/white	Puce	750.00	900.00	450.00

Note: Pair with Hare, model RW2892.

RW2892
HARE

Modeller: Stella R. Crofts
Height: 3", 7.6 cm
Colour: Brown and white hare; green base
Issued: 1931

Colourways	*Backstamp*	*U.S. $*	*Price Can. $*	*U.K. £*
Brown/white	Puce	750.00	900.00	450.00

Note: Pair with Greyhounds, model RW2891.

RW2893
PELICAN ASHTRAY

Modeller: Stella R. Crofts
Height: 3 ¾", 9.5 cm
Colour: White with grey highlights; yellow beak; blue or grey tray
Issued: 1931

Colourways	*Backstamp*	*U.S. $*	*Price Can. $*	*U.K. £*
White/grey/yellow/blue	Puce	200.00	300.00	150.00

RW2894
BOY WITH DONKEY

Modeller: Stella R. Crofts
Height: 6", 15.0 cm
Colour: Blue clothing; brown hair; grey donkey
Issued: 1931-by 1940

Colourways	*Backstamp*	*U.S. $*	*Price Can. $*	*U.K. £*
Blue/brown/grey	Puce	1,900.00	2,375.00	950.00

RW2895
GIRAFFES

Modeller: Stella R. Crofts
Height: 8", 20.3 cm
Colour: Brown and cream; green base
Issued: 1931

Colourways	*Backstamp*	*U.S. $*	*Price* *Can. $*	*U.K. £*
Brown and cream	Puce	1,200.00	1,600.00	800.00

Note: Model RW2895 was available by special order only.

RW2896
CALF

Modeller: Stella R. Crofts
Height: 2 ¼", 5.7 cm
Colour: Light fawn; green base
Issued: 1931-by 1940

Colourways	*Backstamp*	*U.S. $*	*Price* *Can. $*	*U.K. £*
Light fawn	Puce	700.00	1,000.00	500.00

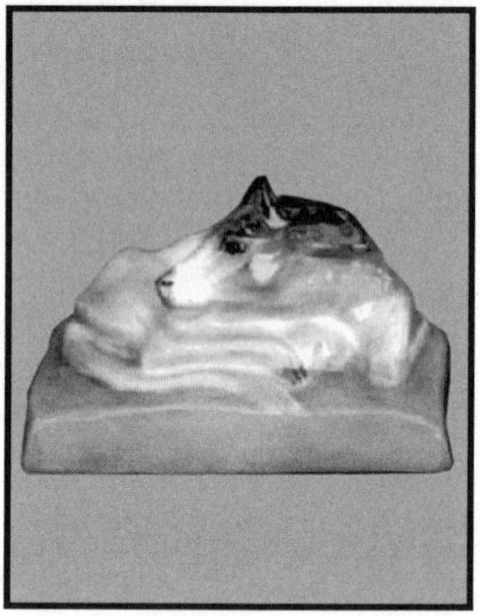

RW2897
CAT (Eating)

Modeller: Stella R. Crofts
Height: 3", 7.6 cm
Colour: 1. Black and grey; fawn base
2. Brown; blue base
Issued: 1931-by 1940

Colourways	*Backstamp*	*U.S. $*	*Price* *Can. $*	*U.K. £*
Coloured (as above)	Puce	625.00	900.00	450.00

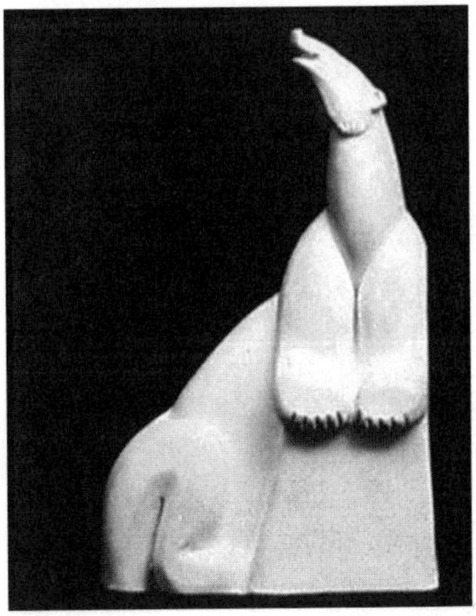

RW2900A
BARBARA (Polar Bear Bookend)

Modeller: Ethelwyn Baker
Height: 6 ½", 16.5 cm
Colour: 1. Coloured
2. White
Issued: 1931-by 1940

Colourways	*Backstamp*	*U.S. $*	*Price Can. $*	*U.K. £*
1. Coloured	Puce	525.00	750.00	375.00
2. White	Green	450.00	650.00	325.00

Note: Pair with Sam (RW2900B). These bookends were available with or without the wooden fitting.

RW2900B
SAM (Polar Bear Bookend)

Modeller: Ethelwyn Baker
Height: 6 ½", 16.5 cm
Colour: 1. Coloured
2. White
Issued: 1931-by 1940

Colourways	*Backstamp*	*U.S. $*	*Price Can. $*	*U.K. £*
1. Coloured	Puce	525.00	750.00	375.00
2. White	Green	450.00	650.00	325.00

Note: Pair with Barabara (RW2900A). These bookends were available with or without the wooden fitting.

RW2925
FOX TOBACCO JAR

Modeller: Doris Lindner
Height: 5 ¾", 14.6 cm
Colour: Coloured fox; cream jar with small or large hunting scene in print and enamel
Issued: 1931
Varieties: Fox (Lying on curved base) RW2950; Fox (Lying, without base) RW3527; Fox Ashtray RW2873

Description	*Backstamp*	*U.S. $*	*Price Can. $*	*U.K. £*
Tobacco Jar	Puce	350.00	500.00	250.00

Note: Produced for Betzemann. Moulds for jar only destroyed 1953.

RW2926
HOUND TOBACCO JAR

Modeller: Doris Lindner
Height: 5 ¼", 13.3 cm
Colour: Coloured hound; cream jar with large or small hunting scene in print and enamel
Issued: 1931
Varieties: Hound (Lying on curved base) RW2951; Hound Ashtray RW2872

Description	*Backstamp*	*U.S. $*	*Price* *Can. $*	*U.K. £*
Tobacco Jar	Puce	375.00	500.00	250.00

Note: Produced for Betzemann. Moulds for jar only destroyed 1953.

RW2927
TERRIER POWDER BOWL / BON BON BOX

Modeller: Doris Lindner
Height: 6", 15.0 cm
Colour: Grey crackle bowl and tinted dog
Issued: 1931
Varieties: Terrier (On plinth) RW2870; Wire-Haired Terrier (Standing, head to right, without plinth) RW3026

Colourways	*Backstamp*	*U.S. $*	*Price* *Can. $*	*U.K. £*
Coloured (as above)	Puce	375.00	500.00	250.00

RW2931
BULL TERRIER "BILL"

Modeller: Doris Lindner
Height: 1. Large: 8", 20.3 cm
2. Small: 4 ½", 11.9 cm
Colour: 1. Large: White dog, green base
2. Small: White dog, yellow base
Issued: 1931-by 1957

Description	*Backstamp*	*U.S. $*	*Price* *Can. $*	*U.K. £*
1. Large	Puce	525.00	700.00	350.00
2. Large	Black	475.00	650.00	325.00
3. Small	Puce	375.00	500.00	250.00
4. Small	Black	325.00	450.00	225.00

Note: These models are also known without the base.

RW2932
SEALYHAM TERRIER "THOMAS" (On plinth)

Modeller: Doris Lindner
Height: 4 ½", 11.9 cm
Colour: White with reddish-brown accents
Issued: 1931-by 1940
Varieties: Sealyham Terrier (Without plinth) RW2934;
Sealyham Terrier on Cigar Tray RW2935

			Price	
Colourways	*Backstamp*	*U.S. $*	*Can. $*	*U.K. £*
White/reddish-brown	Puce	375.00	500.00	250.00

RW2934
SEALYHAM TERRIER (Without plinth)

Modeller: Doris Lindner
Height: 4", 10.1 cm
Colour: White with reddish-brown accents
Issued: 1931-by 1940
Varieties: Sealyham Terrier "Thomas" (On plinth) RW2932;
Sealyham Terrier on Cigar Tray RW2935

			Price	
Colourways	*Backstamp*	*U.S. $*	*Can. $*	*U.K. £*
White/reddish-brown	Puce	375.00	500.00	250.00

RW2935
SEALYHAM TERRIER ON CIGAR TRAY

Modeller: Doris Lindner
Height: 4 ½", 11.9 cm
Colour: White with reddish-brown accents
Issued: 1931-by 1940
Varieties: Sealyham Terrier "Thomas" (On plinth) RW2932;
Sealyham Terrier (Without plinth) RW2934

			Price	
Colourways	*Backstamp*	*U.S. $*	*Can. $*	*U.K. £*
White/reddish-brown	Puce	425.00	700.00	350.00

RW2941
PEKINESE (Standing)

Modeller: Doris Lindner
Height: 2", 5.0 cm
Colour: 1. Reddish-brown
2. White
Issued: 1932-by 1957
Series: Small Dogs

Colourways	*Backstamp*	*U.S. $*	*Price* *Can. $*	*U.K. £*
1. Coloured (as above)	Puce	200.00	250.00	130.00
2. Coloured (as above)	Black	150.00	200.00	100.00
3. White	Green	175.00	225.00	110.00

RW2942
AIREDALE TERRIER / WIRE-HAIRED TERRIER (Seated)

Modeller: Doris Lindner
Height: 2 ½", 6.4 cm
Colour: **Airedale Terrier:**
1. Brown with darker brown markings
Wire-Haired Terrier:
2. White with brown markings
3. White
Issued: 1932-by 1957
Series: Small Dogs

Description	*Backstamp*	*U.S. $*	*Price* *Can. $*	*U.K. £*
1. Airedale Terrier	Puce	250.00	325.00	150.00
2. Airedale Terrier	Black	200.00	250.00	130.00
3. Wire-Haired Terrier	Puce	250.00	325.00	150.00
4. Wire-Haired Terrier	Black	200.00	250.00	130.00
5. White	Green	150.00	200.00	100.00

RW2943
DANDIE DINMONT TERRIER

Modeller: Doris Lindner
Height: 2", 5.0 cm
Colour: 1. Grey
2. Light brown and cream
3. White
Issued: 1932-by 1957
Series: Small Dogs

Colourways	*Backstamp*	*U.S. $*	*Price* *Can. $*	*U.K. £*
1. Coloured (as above)	Puce	200.00	250.00	125.00
2. Coloured (as above)	Black	150.00	200.00	100.00
3. White	Green	150.00	200.00	100.00

RW2944
COCKER SPANIEL (Style One - No space between front legs) / ENGLISH SPRINGER SPANIEL (Standing)

Modeller: Doris Lindner
Height: 2 ¼", 5.7 cm
Colour: **Cocker Spaniel:**
1. Black
2. Red
English Springer Spaniel:
3. White with black markings
4. White with liver markings
5. White
Issued: 1932
Series: Small Dogs

			Price	
Description	*Backstamp*	*U.S. $*	*Can. $*	*U.K. £*
1. Coloured (as above)	Puce	200.00	250.00	150.00
2. White	Green	150.00	200.00	100.00

RW2945
ENGLISH BULLDOG

Modeller: Doris Lindner
Height: 2 ½", 6.4 cm
Colour: 1. Brindle
2. White with black markings
3. White with reddish-brown markings
4. White
Issued: 1932
Series: Small Dogs

			Price	
Colourways	*Backstamp*	*U.S. $*	*Can. $*	*U.K. £*
1. Coloured (as above)	Puce	300.00	300.00	150.00
2. White	Green	200.00	200.00	100.00

RW2946
ABERDEEN TOY TERRIER / SCOTTISH TERRIER (Standing)

Modeller: Doris Lindner
Height: 2 ¼", 5.7 cm
Colour: 1. Black
2. White
Issued: 1932
Series: Small Dogs

			Price	
Colourways	*Backstamp*	*U.S. $*	*Can. $*	*U.K. £*
1. Black	Puce	350.00	300.00	130.00
2. White	Green	350.00	300.00	130.00

Note: Model RW2946 could be painted as either an Aberdeen Toy Terrier or as a Scottish Terrier.

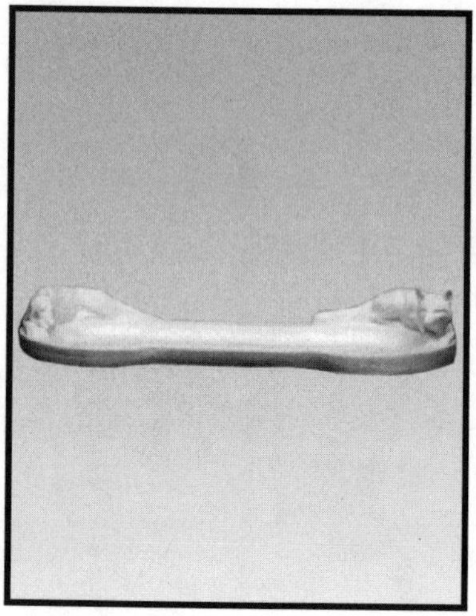

RW2947
FOX AND HOUND PEN TRAY

Modeller: Doris Lindner
Size: Unknown
Colour: Cream tray; reddish-brown fox; white hound with brown and black markings
Issued: 1932

Colourways	*Backstamp*	*U.S. $*	*Price Can. $*	*U.K. £*
Cream/reddish-brown/white	Puce	350.00	500.00	250.00

Note: Produced for Betzemann for mounting.
Models used on this pen tray are Fox (Lying, on curved base) RW2950 and Hound (Lying, on curved base) RW2951.

RW2950
FOX (Lying, on curved base)

Modeller: Doris Lindner
Height: 2", 5.0 cm
Colour: Chestnut red fox; cream base
Issued: 1932
Varieties: Fox (Lying, without base) RW3527; Fox Ashtray RW2873; Fox Tobacco Jar RW2925

Colourways	*Backstamp*	*U.S. $*	*Price Can. $*	*U.K. £*
Chestnut red	Puce	250.00	350.00	175.00

Note: Produced for Betzemann for mounting.
Model RW2950 was also used to make the Fox and Hound Pen Tray RW2947.

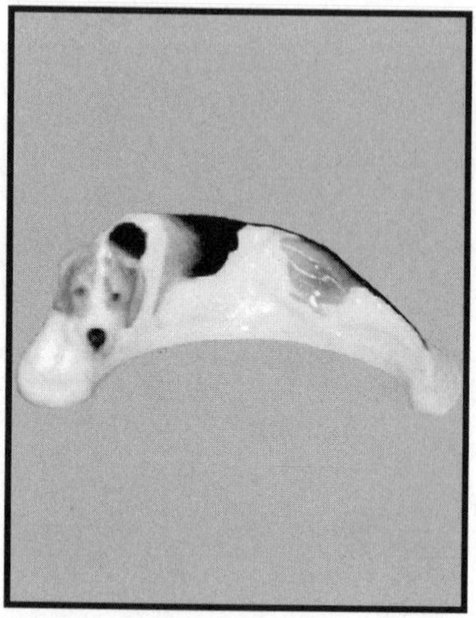

RW2951
HOUND (Lying, on curved base)

Modeller: Doris Lindner
Height: 2", 5.0 cm
Colour: White with chestnut brown and black markings; cream base
Issued: 1932
Varieties: Hound Ashtray RW2872; Hound Tobacco Jar RW2926

Colourways	*Backstamp*	*U.S. $*	*Price Can. $*	*U.K. £*
White/chestnut brown	Puce	250.00	350.00	175.00

Note: Produced for Betzemann for mounting and sold through Aspreys and Thomas Goode, London, England.
Model RW2951 was also used to make the Fox and Hound Pen Tray RW2947.

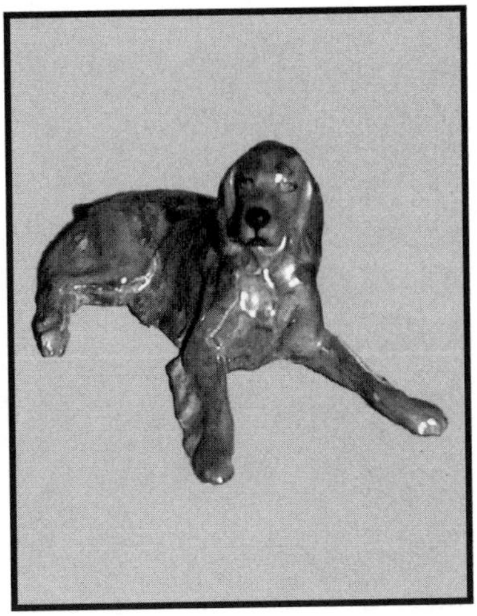

RW2952
SETTER (Without plinth)

Modeller: Doris Lindner
Height: 2 ½", 6.4 cm
Colour: Chestnut-red
Issued: 1932
Varieties: Setter (On plinth) RW2871

Colourways	*Backstamp*	*U.S. $*	*Price Can. $*	*U.K. £*
Chestnut-red	Puce	325.00	450.00	225.00

RW2993
FOX (Seated)

Modeller: Doris Lindner
Height: 7", 17.8 cm
Colour: Red-brown, white and dark brown
Issued: 1932-1974

Backstamp	*U.S. $*	*Price Can. $*	*U.K. £*
1. Puce	500.00	700.00	350.00
2. Black	425.00	600.00	300.00

Note: Also mounted as a bookend by Betzemann.

RW2994
HOUND (Seated)

Modeller: Doris Lindner
Height: 6 ¾", 17.2 cm
Colour: White with brown markings
Issued: 1932-1974

Backstamp	*U.S. $*	*Price Can. $*	*U.K. £*
1. Puce	450.00	600.00	300.00
2. Black	400.00	500.00	250.00

Note: Also mounted as a bookend by Betzemann.

RW2997
FOX (Lying, on straight base)

Modeller: Doris Lindner
Length: 4 ½", 11.9 cm
Colour: Reddish-brown
Issued: 1932
Varieties: Fox (Lying straight, without base) RW3570

Colourways	*Backstamp*	*U.S. $*	*Price Can. $*	*U.K. £*
Reddish-brown	Puce	325.00	450.00	225.00

Note: Produced for Betzemann for mounting.

RW2998
HOUND (Lying, on straight base)

Modeller: Doris Lindner
Length: 4 ½", 11.9 cm
Colour: White with dark brown and black markings
Issued: 1932
Varieties: Hound (Lying straight, without base) RW3571

Colourways	*Backstamp*	*U.S. $*	*Price Can. $*	*U.K. £*
White/brown	Puce	325.00	450.00	225.00

Note: Produced for Betzemann for mounting.

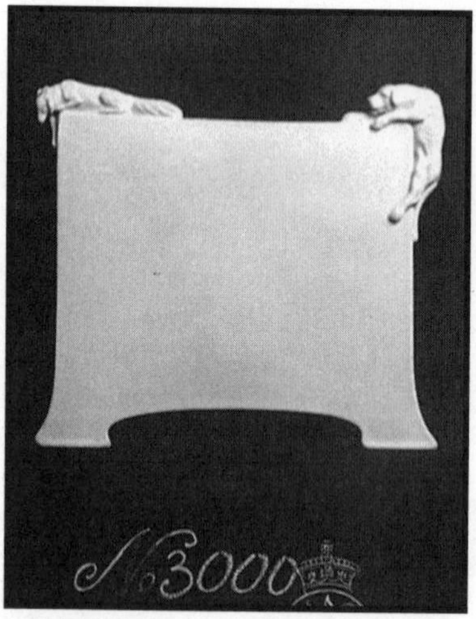

RW3000
FOX AND HOUND CALENDAR

Modeller: Possibly Doris Lindner
Height: 5 ½", 14.0 cm
Colour: Unknown
Issued: 1932-by 1953

Backstamp	*U.S. $*	*Price Can. $*	*U.K. £*
1. Puce	500.00	700.00	350.00
2. Black	425.00	600.00	300.00

Note: This calendar was produced exclusively for Betzemann.

RW3013
SEAL

Modeller: Unknown
Height: Unknown
Colour: Unknown
Issued: 1932

Colourways	*Backstamp*	*U.S. $*	*Price Can. $*	*U.K. £*
Unknown	Possibly not put into production			

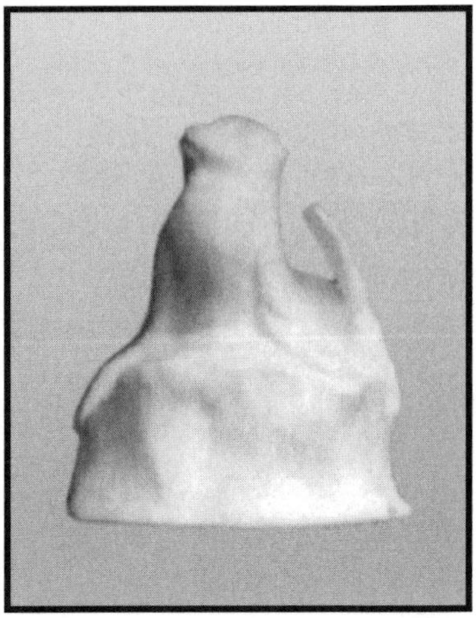

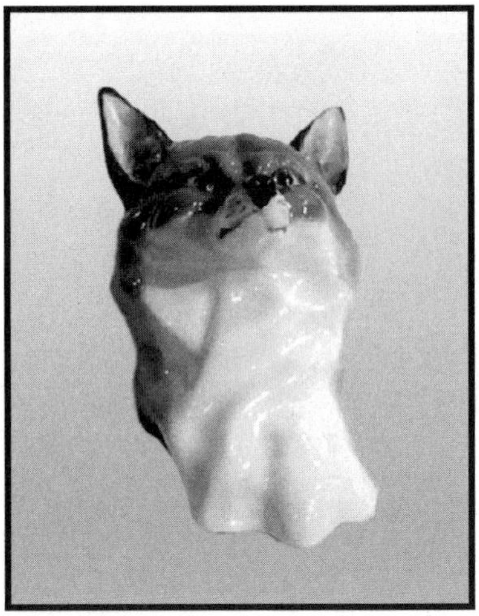

RW3024
FOX HEAD (Wall mount)

Modeller: Doris Lindner
Height: 4", 10.1 cm
Colour: White and brown
Issued: 1933-by 1960s
Series: Wall Mounts

Backstamp	*U.S. $*	*Price Can. $*	*U.K. £*
1. Puce	350.00	500.00	250.00
2. Black	275.00	400.00	200.00

Note: The head of model RW2993 was used to make this wall mount.

RW3025
HOUND HEAD (Wall mount)

Modeller: Doris Lindner
Height: 4", 10.1 cm
Colour: White and brown
Issued: 1933-by 1960s
Series: Wall Mounts

Backstamp	*U.S. $*	*Price Can. $*	*U.K. £*
1. Puce	350.00	500.00	250.00
2. Black	275.00	400.00	200.00

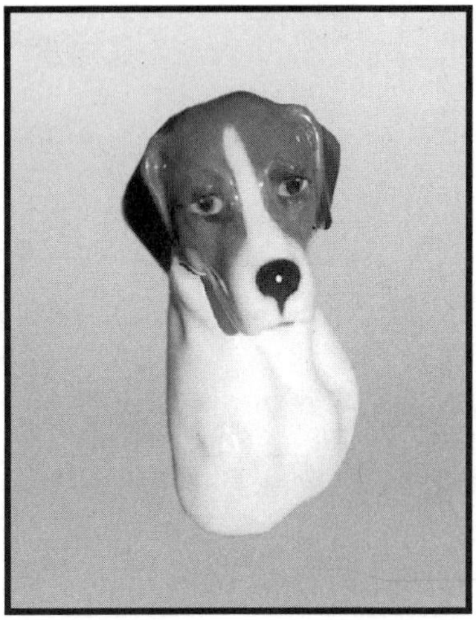

Note: The head of model RW2994 was used to make this wall mount.

RW3026
AIREDALE TERRIER/WIRE-HAIRED TERRIER
(Standing, head to right, without plinth)

Modeller: Doris Lindner
Height: 2 ½", 6.4 cm
Colour: 1. **Airedale Terrier:** Golden brown with darker brown shading
2. **Wire-Haired Terrier:** White with reddish-brown
Issued: 1933-1957
Varieties: Terrier (On plinth) RW2870;
Terrier Powder Bowl / Bon Bon Box RW2927
Series: Small Dogs

			Price	
Description	*Backstamp*	*U.S. $*	*Can. $*	*U.K. £*
1. Airedale Terrier	Puce	300.00	350.00	150.00
2. Airedale Terrier	Black	250.00	300.00	125.00
3. Wire-Haired Terrier	Puce	300.00	350.00	150.00
4. Wire-Haired Terrier	Black	250.00	300.00	125.00

RW3027
AIREDALE TERRIER /WIRE-HAIRED TERRIER (Standing, head to left)

Modeller: Doris Lindner
Height: 2 ¾", 6.9 cm
Colour: 1. **Airedale Terrier:** Golden brown with darker brown shading
2. **Wire-Haired Terrier:** White with reddish-brown and black patches
Issued: 1933-1957
Series: Small Dogs

			Price	
Description	*Backstamp*	*U.S. $*	*Can. $*	*U.K. £*
1. Airedale Terrier	Puce	350.00	350.00	150.00
2. Airedale Terrier	Black	275.00	300.00	125.00
3. Wire-Haired Terrier	Puce	325.00	350.00	150.00
4. Wire-Haired Terrier	Black	250.00	300.00	125.00

RW3028
SEALYHAM TERRIER

Modeller: Doris Lindner
Height: 2", 5.0 cm
Colour: White with golden brown markings
Issued: 1933-1957
Series: Small Dogs

		Price	
Backstamp	*U.S. $*	*Can. $*	*U.K. £*
1. Puce	225.00	300.00	150.00
2. Black	175.00	250.00	125.00

RW3029
SCOTTISH TERRIER (Seated)

Modeller: Doris Lindner
Height: 2", 5.0 cm
Colour: 1. Black
2. White
Issued: 1933-by 1957
Series: Small Dogs

			Price	
Colourways	*Backstamp*	*U.S. $*	*Can. $*	*U.K. £*
1. Black	Puce	250.00	350.00	150.00
2. Black	Black	200.00	300.00	125.00
3. White	Puce	250.00	350.00	150.00
4. White	Green	200.00	300.00	125.00

RW3031
SALMON
Style One

Modeller: Unknown
Size: Large
Colour: 1. Coloured
2. White
Issued: 1933

			Price	
Colourways	*Backstamp*	*U.S. $*	*Can. $*	*U.K. £*
1. Coloured	Puce	500.00	700.00	350.00
2. White	Green	225.00	300.00	150.00

Note: Produced for H. Grant, Torquay.

RW3032
TROUT
Style One

Modeller: Unknown
Size: Large
Colour: 1. Coloured
2. White
Issued: 1933

			Price	
Colourways	*Backstamp*	*U.S. $*	*Can. $*	*U.K. £*
1. Coloured	Puce	500.00	700.00	350.00
2. White	Green	225.00	300.00	150.00

Note: Produced for H. Grant, Torquay.

RW3033
COCKER SPANIEL (Standing)
Style Two (Front legs apart)

Modeller: Doris Lindner
Height: 2", 5.0 cm
Colour: 1. Black
2. Golden
3. White with black markings
4. White with dark brown markings
Issued: 1933-1957
Series: Small Dogs

Backstamp	*U.S. $*	*Price* *Can. $*	*U.K. £*
1. Puce	225.00	275.00	125.00
2. Black	175.00	225.00	100.00

RW3034
PEKINESE (Seated)

Modeller: Doris Lindner
Height: 2", 5.0 cm
Colour: Golden brown and cream
Issued: 1933-1957
Series: Small Dogs

Backstamp	*U.S. $*	*Price* *Can. $*	*U.K. £*
1. Puce	225.00	275.00	125.00
2. Black	175.00	225.00	100.00

RW3035
SALMON
Style Two

Modeller: Unknown
Size: Small
Colour: 1. Coloured
2. White
Issued: 1933

Colourways	*Backstamp*	*U.S. $*	*Price* *Can. $*	*U.K. £*
1. Coloured	Puce	500.00	700.00	350.00
2. White	Green	225.00	300.00	150.00

Note: Produced for H. Grant, Torquay.

RW3036
PIKE

Modeller: Unknown
Size: Small
Colour: 1. Coloured
2. White
Issued: 1933

			Price	
Colourways	*Backstamp*	*U.S. $*	*Can. $*	*U.K. £*
1. Coloured	Puce	500.00	700.00	350.00
2. White	Green	225.00	300.00	150.00

Note: Produced for H. Grant, Torquay.

RW3037
TROUT
Style Two

Modeller: Unknown
Size: Small
Colour: 1. Coloured
2. White
Issued: 1933

			Price	
Colourways	*Backstamp*	*U.S. $*	*Can. $*	*U.K. £*
1. Coloured	Puce	500.00	700.00	350.00
2. White	Green	225.00	300.00	150.00

Note: Produced for H. Grant, Torquay.

RW3038
ROACH

Modeller: Unknown
Size: Small
Colour: 1. Coloured
2. White
Issued: 1933

			Price	
Colourways	*Backstamp*	*U.S. $*	*Can. $*	*U.K. £*
1. Coloured	Puce	500.00	700.00	350.00
2. White	Green	225.00	300.00	150.00

Note: Produced for H. Grant, Torquay.

RW3039
CARP

Modeller: Unknown
Size: Small
Colour: 1. Coloured
2. White
Issued: 1933

Colourways	*Backstamp*	*U.S. $*	*Price Can. $*	*U.K. £*
1. Coloured	Puce	500.00	700.00	350.00
2. White	Green	225.00	300.00	150.00

Note: Produced for H. Grant, Torquay.

RW3062
POLAR BEAR BOOKEND (Bear bending)

Modeller: Doris Lindner
Height: 3 ¼", 8.3 cm
Colour: White; brown and purple highlights
Issued: 1934
Varieties: Polar Bear Ashtray (Bear bending) RW3185

Colourways	*Backstamp*	*U.S. $*	*Price Can. $*	*U.K. £*
White/brown/purple	Puce	450.00	600.00	300.00

Note: Produced for H. Grant, Torquay.

RW3063
POLAR BEAR BOOKEND (Bear seated, looking up)

Modeller: Doris Lindner
Height: 4 ¾", 12.1 cm
Colour: White; brown and purple highlights
Issued: 1934
Varieties: Polar Bear Ashtray (Bear seated, looking up) RW3184

Colourways	*Backstamp*	*U.S. $*	*Price Can. $*	*U.K. £*
White/brown/purple	Puce	450.00	600.00	300.00

Note: Produced for H. Grant, Torquay.

RW3085
POODLE, CHAMPION "SPRIGGAN BELL"

Modeller: Doris Lindner
Height: 8 ½", 21.6 cm
Colour: 1. Dark and light brown
2. White
Issued: 1935

			Price	
Colourways	*Backstamp*	*U.S. $*	*Can. $*	*U.K. £*
1. Coloured (as above)	Gold	1,000.00	1,350.00	450.00
2. White	Green	750.00	1,000.00	325.00

RW3093
PENGUIN (Head forward)

Modeller: Doris Lindner
Height: 4 ¾", 12.1 cm
Colour: White with blue-grey, yellow and black markings; orange beak
Issued: 1935-by 1940

			Price	
Colourways	*Backstamp*	*U.S. $*	*Can. $*	*U.K. £*
White/blue-grey	Puce	550.00	750.00	375.00

RW3094
PENGUIN (Raised beak)

Modeller: Doris Lindner
Height: 4 ¾", 12.1 cm
Colour: White with blue-grey, yellow and black markings; orange beak
Issued: 1935-by 1940

			Price	
Colourways	*Backstamp*	*U.S. $*	*Can. $*	*U.K. £*
White/blue-grey	Puce	550.00	750.00	375.00

RW3096
ELEPHANT
Style One

Modeller:	E. Evans
Height:	3 ½", 8.9 cm
Size:	Large
Colour:	1. Green enamel 2. White
Issued:	1935

Colourways	*Backstamp*	*U.S. $*	*Price* *Can. $*	*U.K. £*
1. Coloured (as above)	Puce	575.00	800.00	400.00
2. White	Green	275.00	400.00	200.00

RW3100
LION

Modeller:	E. Evans
Height:	3", 7.6 cm
Colour:	Golden brown
Issued:	1935-by 1940

Colourways	*Backstamp*	*U.S. $*	*Price* *Can. $*	*U.K. £*
Golden brown	Puce	425.00	600.00	300.00

RW3101
TIGER

Modeller:	E. Evans
Height:	2 ½", 6.4 cm
Colour:	Unknown
Issued:	1935-by 1940

Colourways	*Backstamp*	*U.S. $*	*Price* *Can. $*	*U.K. £*
Unknown	Puce	425.00	600.00	300.00

RW3102
ELEPHANT
Style Two

Modeller: E. Evans
Height: 2 ½", 6.4 cm
Size: Small
Colour: 1. Green enamel
2. White
Issued: 1935

Colourways	*Backstamp*	*U.S. $*	*Price Can. $*	*U.K. £*
1. Coloured (as above)	Puce	575.00	800.00	400.00
2. White	Green	275.00	400.00	200.00

RW3110
BEAR

Modeller: Possibly E. Evans
Height: 2 ½", 6.4 cm
Colour: Brown
Issued: 1935-by 1940

Colourways	*Backstamp*	*U.S. $*	*Price Can. $*	*U.K. £*
Brown	Puce	425.00	600.00	300.00

RW3112
AMERICAN REDSTART (Cock)
(Setophaga Ruticilla)

Modeller: Dorothy Doughty
Height: 7 ¾", 19.7 cm
Colour: Purple and pink bird; green fir branches
Issued: 1935 in a limited edition of 66
Series: Doughty American Birds

Colourways	*Backstamp*	*U.S. $*	*Price Can. $*	*U.K. £*
Purple/pink/green	Puce	750.00	1,000.00	500.00

Note: Commissioned by Alex Dickens, USA.

RW3113
AMERICAN REDSTART (Hen)
(Setophaga Ruticilla)

Modeller: Dorothy Doughty
Height: 7 ¾", 19.7 cm
Colour: Yellowish-green and grey-brown; green fir branches
Issued: 1935 in a limited edition of 66
Series: Doughty American Birds

Colourways	*Backstamp*	*U.S. $*	Price *Can. $*	*U.K. £*
Yellowish-green/grey-brown	Puce	750.00	1,000.00	500.00

Note: Commissioned by Alex Dickens, USA.

RW3114
AT THE MEET

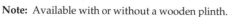

Modeller: Doris Lindner
Height: 7 ¼", 18.4 cm
Colour: 1. Rider: Black habit, hat and boots
Horse: Grey
2. Rider: Navy habit, hat and boots
Horse: Bay
3. White
Issued: 1935-1981
Series: Equestrian

Colourways	*Backstamp*	*U.S. $*	Price *Can. $*	*U.K. £*
1. Coloured (as above)	Puce	1,250.00	1,500.00	750.00
2. Coloured (as above)	Black	1,000.00	1,250.00	600.00
3. White	Green	325.00	450.00	200.00

Note: Available with or without a wooden plinth.

RW3115
HUNTSMAN AND HOUNDS

Modeller: Doris Lindner
Height: Without plinth: 7 ½", 19.1 cm
With plinth: 9", 22.9 cm
Colour: 1. Rider: Red riding habit; white jodhpurs and cravat; black hat; metal whip
Horse: Light grey
Dogs: White with light brown and black patches
2. White
Issued: 1936-1981
Series: Equestrian

Colourways	*Backstamp*	*U.S. $*	Price *Can. $*	*U.K. £*
1. Coloured (as above)	Puce	1,500.00	1,850.00	900.00
2. Coloured (as above)	Black	1,250.00	1,500.00	750.00
3. White	Green	325.00	450.00	200.00

Note: Available with or without a wooden plinth.

RW3116
OVER THE STICKS

Modeller: Doris Lindner
Height: Without plinth: 7 ¼", 18.4 cm
With plinth: 9 ¾", 24.7 cm
Colour: 1. Rider: Various coloured silks
Horse: Chestnut
2. White
Issued: 1936-1986
Series: Equestrian

Colourways	*Backstamp*	*U.S. $*	*Price* *Can. $*	*U.K. £*
1. Coloured (as above)	Puce	900.00	1,150.00	450.00
2. Coloured (as above)	Black	700.00	900.00	400.00
3. White	Green	325.00	450.00	200.00

Note: Many colourway variations of this model may exist as the rider's silks could be painted to order. Available with or without a wooden plinth.

RW3117
CANTERING TO THE POST

Modeller: Doris Lindner
Height: Without plinth: 6 ¼", 15.9 cm
With plinth: 7 ¼", 18.4 cm
Colour: 1. Rider: Various coloured silks
Horse: Bay
2. White
Issued: 1936-1986
Series: Equestrian

Colourways	*Backstamp*	*U.S. $*	*Price* *Can. $*	*U.K. £*
1. Coloured (as above)	Puce	900.00	1,150.00	450.00
2. Coloured (as above)	Black	700.00	900.00	400.00
3. White	Green	325.00	450.00	200.00

Note: Many colourway variations of this model may exist as the rider's silks could be painted to order. Available with or without a wooden plinth.

RW3118
PEKINESE PUPPIES (Four)

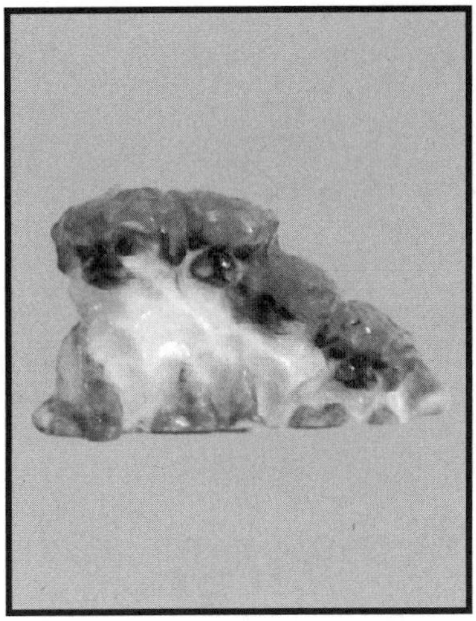

Modeller: Doris Lindner
Height: 2 ½", 6.4 cm
Colour: 1. Golden brown and cream
2. White
Issued: 1935-c.1950s

Colourways	*Backstamp*	*U.S. $*	*Price* *Can. $*	*U.K. £*
1. Coloured (as above)	Puce	500.00	700.00	350.00
2. Coloured (as above)	Black	450.00	650.00	325.00
3. White	Green	300.00	350.00	175.00

RW3119
SEALYHAM TERRIER PUPPIES CIGARETTE BOX

Modeller:	Doris Lindner
Height:	3 ¼", 8.3 cm
Colour:	Dogs: White with brown highlights Box: Brown
Issued:	1936-by 1953

Backstamp	*U.S. $*	*Price* *Can. $*	*U.K. £*
1. Puce	550.00	750.00	375.00
2. Black	500.00	650.00	325.00

RW3120
SPANIELS' CALENDAR

Modeller:	Doris Lindner
Height:	3 ½", 8.9 cm
Colour:	Black and blue roan spaniels; green base
Issued:	1936-by 1953

Backstamp	*U.S. $*	*Price* *Can. $*	*U.K. £*
1. Puce	425.00	600.00	300.00
2. Black	350.00	500.00	250.00

Note: Produced for Betzemann for mounting.

RW3121
TIGER (On plinth)

Modeller:	Guéro
Height:	5 ¼", 13.3 cm
Colour:	White
Issued:	1936

Colourways	*Backstamp*	*U.S. $*	*Price* *Can. $*	*U.K. £*
White	Green	850.00	1,250.00	600.00

Note: Available with or without an oak plinth.

RW3123
MAYTIME (With base)

Modeller: Doris Lindner
Height: 3 ¾", 9.5 cm
Colour: 1. Creamy white; black feet, nose, eyes, inner ear; green base
2. White
Issued: 1936-c.1950s
Varieties: Maytime (Without base) RW3516

			Price	
Colourways	*Backstamp*	*U.S. $*	*Can. $*	*U.K. £*
1. Coloured (as above)	Green	450.00	650.00	325.00
2. White	Green	200.00	300.00	150.00

RW3124
GOAT (Licking hind leg, with base)

Modeller: Henri Bargas
Height: 5", 12.7 cm
Colour: 1. Creamy-white with black markings, green base
2. White
Issued: 1936-c.1950s
Varieties: Goat (Licking hind leg, without base) RW3531
Series: Goats

			Price	
Colourways	*Backstamp*	*U.S. $*	*Can. $*	*U.K. £*
1. Coloured (as above)	Black	525.00	750.00	375.00
2. White	Green	200.00	300.00	150.00

Note: A wooden plinth was available for this model.

RW3125
GOAT (Head raised, with base)

Modeller: Henri Bargas
Height: 5 ½", 14.0 cm
Colour: 1. Creamy with black markings; green base
2. White
Issued: 1936-c.1950s
Varieties: Goat (Head raised, without base) RW3530
Series: Goats

			Price	
Colourways	*Backstamp*	*U.S. $*	*Can. $*	*U.K. £*
1. Coloured (as above)	Black	525.00	750.00	375.00
2. White	Green	200.00	300.00	150.00

Note: A wooden plinth was available for this model.

RW3130
SPANIEL PUPPIES (Three)

Modeller: Doris Lindner
Height: 2", 5.0 cm
Colour: 1. Two black and one golden brown
2. Two golden brown and one black
Issued: 1936-c.1950s

Backstamp	*U.S. $*	*Price* *Can. $*	*U.K. £*
1. Puce	350.00	600.00	300.00
2. Black	300.00	500.00	250.00

RW3131
YOUNG FOXES (Three)

Modeller: Doris Lindner
Height: 2 ½", 6.4 cm
Colour: Reddish-brown and white
Issued: 1936-c.1950s

Backstamp	*U.S. $*	*Price* *Can. $*	*U.K. £*
1. Puce	425.00	600.00	300.00
2. Black	375.00	500.00	250.00

RW3132
FOXHOUND PUPPIES (Three)

Modeller: Doris Lindner
Height: 2 ½", 6.4 cm
Colour: White with light brown faces
Issued: 1936-c.1950s

Backstamp	*U.S. $*	*Price* *Can. $*	*U.K. £*
1. Puce	425.00	600.00	300.00
2. Black	375.00	500.00	275.00

RW3133
BULLDOG PUPPIES (Two)

Modeller: Doris Lindner
Height: 2", 5.0 cm
Colour: 1. Left puppy: White with light brown patches
Right puppy: White with dark brown patches;
name on bowl "Puppy"
2. Left puppy: White with light brown patches
Right puppy: Brindle;
name on bowl "Puppy"
Issued: 1936-c.1950s

Backstamp	*U.S. $*	*Price Can. $*	*U.K. £*
1. Puce	550.00	750.00	375.00
2. Black	450.00	650.00	325.00

RW3134
AMERICAN GOLDFINCH AND THISTLE (Cock)
(Spinus Tristis Tristis)

Modeller: Dorothy Doughty
Height: 6 ½", 16.5 cm
Colour: Yellow and brown bird; grey and green thistle
Plinth: Wooden
Issued: 1936 in a limited edition of 250
Series: Doughty American Birds

Colourways	*Backstamp*	*U.S. $*	*Price Can. $*	*U.K. £*
Yellow/brown/grey/green	Black	850.00	1,250.00	600.00

Note: Commissioned by Alex Dickens, USA.

RW3135
AMERICAN GOLDFINCH AND THISTLE (Hen)
(Spinus Tristis Tristis)

Modeller: Dorothy Doughty
Height: 6 ½", 16.5 cm
Colour: Yellow and brown bird; mauve and green thistle
Plinth: Wooden
Issued: 1936 in a limited edition of 250
Series: Doughty American Birds

Colourways	*Backstamp*	*U.S. $*	*Price Can. $*	*U.K. £*
Yellow/brown/mauve/green	Black	850.00	1,250.00	600.00

Note: Commissioned by Alex Dickens, USA.

RW3136
BLUEBIRD AND APPLE BLOSSOM (Hen)
(Sialia Sialis)

Modeller:	Dorothy Doughty
Height:	9 ½", 24.0 cm
Colour:	Blue and russet bird with twig in its mouth; pink and white apple blossom; green leaves
Plinth:	Wooden
Issued:	1936 in a limited edition of 350
Series:	Doughty American Birds

Colourways	*Backstamp*	*Price* *U.S. $*	*Can. $*	*U.K. £*
Blue/russet/pink/white/green	Black	900.00	1,250.00	650.00

Note: Commissioned by Alex Dickens, USA.

RW3137
BLUEBIRD AND APPLE BLOSSOM (Cock)
(Sialia Sialis)

Modeller:	Dorothy Doughty
Height:	9 ½", 24.0 cm
Colour:	Blue and russet bird; pink and white blossom; green leaves
Plinth:	Wooden
Issued:	1936 in a limited edition of 350
Series:	Doughty American Birds

Colourways	*Backstamp*	*Price* *U.S. $*	*Can. $*	*U.K. £*
Blue/russet/pink/white/green	Black	900.00	1,250.00	650.00

Note: Commissioned by Alex Dickens, USA.

RW3141
KITTENS (Three)

Modeller:	Doris Lindner
Height:	2 ¼", 6.4 cm
Colour:	Black and white kitten; brown and white kitten; grey and white kitten
Issued:	1936-c.1950s

Backstamp	*Price* *U.S. $*	*Can. $*	*U.K. £*
1. Puce	675.00	900.00	475.00
2. Black	600.00	800.00	425.00

RW3146
CALVES (With base)

Modeller: Doris Lindner
Height: 4", 10.1 cm
Colour: Reddish-brown and white
Issued: 1936-c.1950s
Varieties: Calves (Without base) RW3515

Colourways	*Backstamp*	*U.S. $*	*Price Can. $*	*U.K. £*
Reddish-brown/white	Green	525.00	750.00	375.00

RW3152
FOALS (With base)

Modeller: Doris Lindner
Height: 5 ½", 14.0 cm
Colour: Light tan; dark tan; light green base
Issued: 1936-c.1950s
Varieties: Foals (Without base) RW3514

Colourways	*Backstamp*	*U.S. $*	*Price Can. $*	*U.K. £*
Light and dark tan	Green	600.00	850.00	425.00

RW3153
KIDS AT PLAY (With base)

Modeller: Doris Lindner
Height: 4 ¾", 12.1 cm
Colour: Grey-blue, black and white; light green base
Issued: 1936-c.1950s
Varieties: Kids at Play (Without base) RW3517
Series: Goats

Colourways	*Backstamp*	*U.S. $*	*Price Can. $*	*U.K. £*
Grey-blue/black/white	Green	450.00	650.00	325.00

RW3155
SHEEP

Modeller: Henri Bargas
Height: 5", 12.7 cm
Colour: 1. Creamy-white with black markings; green base
2. White
Issued: 1936-c.1950s

Colourways	*Backstamp*	*U.S. $*	*Price Can. $*	*U.K. £*
1. Coloured (as above)	Black	300.00	450.00	225.00
2. White	Green	150.00	200.00	100.00

Note: A wooden plinth was available for this model.

RW3156
ASHTRAY (With dog)

Modeller: Doris Lindner
Size: 3 ½" x 4 ½", 8.9 x 11.9 cm
Colour: Light green ashtray; various dogs
Issued: 1933-c.1940s

Colourways	*Backstamp*	*U.S. $*	*Price Can. $*	*U.K. £*
Various	Puce	300.00	450.00	225.00

Note: This ashtray base was available with 'assorted dogs.'

Photograph not available at press time

RW3162
SCOTTISH TERRIER PUPPIES ON CIGARETTE BOX

Modeller: Doris Lindner
Height: 3 ½", 8.9 cm
Colour: Unknown
Issued: 1936

Colourways	*Backstamp*	*U.S. $*	*Price Can. $*	*U.K. £*
Unknown	Puce	525.00	750.00	375.00

RW3163
POLO PLAYER

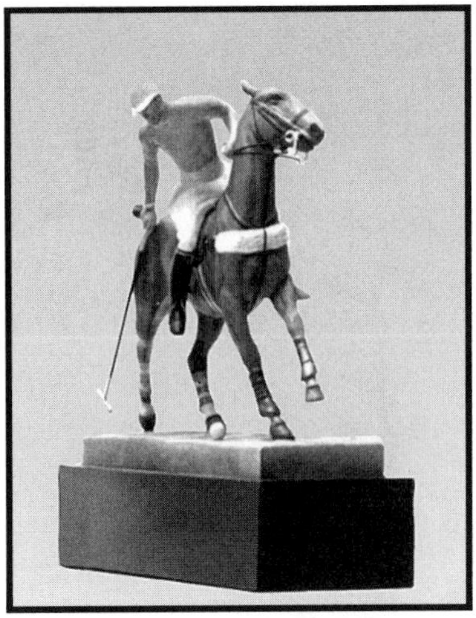

Modeller:	Doris Lindner
Height:	Without plinth: 6 ¾", 17.2 cm With plinth: 8 ¼", 21.0 cm
Colour:	1. Jockey: Blue, red and yellow shirt; white jodhpurs and cap; black boots; brown metal polo stick and reins Horse: Chestnut; gloss or matt 2. Jockey: Yellow shirt; white jodhpurs and cap; brown metal polo stick and reins Horse: Chestnut; gloss or matt
Issued:	1936-1981

		Price		
Colourways	*Backstamp*	*U.S. $*	*Can. $*	*U.K. £*
1. Coloured (as above)	Puce	1,150.00	1,500.00	650.00
2. Coloured (as above)	Black	1,000.00	1,350.00	550.00

Note: Available with or without a wooden plinth.

RW3164
HOG HUNTING

Modeller:	Doris Lindner
Height:	Without plinth: 6 ¾", 17.2 cm With plinth: 8 ½", 21.6 cm
Colour:	Rider: Khaki clothes and hat; painted metal spear Horse: Bay Hog: Dark grey
Issued:	1936-1981

	Price		
Backstamp	*U.S. $*	*Can. $*	*U.K. £*
1. Puce	1,150.00	1,450.00	580.00
2. Black	950.00	1,200.00	480.00

Note: Available with or without a wooden plinth.

RW3165
BANBURY CROSS

Modeller:	Geraldine Blake
Height:	8", 20.3 cm
Colour:	Unknown
Issued:	1936-c.1950s

		Price		
Colourways	*Backstamp*	*U.S. $*	*Can. $*	*U.K. £*
Unknown	Puce	1,500.00	1,850.00	900.00

Note: Available with or without a wooden plinth.

RW3166
HIGHWAYMAN

Modeller: Geraldine Blake
Height: 8 ½", 21.6 cm
Colour: Rider: Pale blue jacket; green shirt; black hat, eye mask and boots
Horse: Black; brown saddle
Issued: 1936-c.1950s

		Price	
Backstamp	*U.S. $*	*Can. $*	*U.K. £*
1. Puce	1,250.00	1,500.00	750.00
2. Black	1,000.00	1,250.00	600.00

Note: Available with or without a wooden plinth.

RW3167
YONDER HE GOES

Modeller: Geraldine Blake
Height: 8", 20.3 cm
Colour: Rider: Red riding habit; white jodhpurs; black hat and boots
Horse: Black
Issued: 1936-c.1950s

			Price	
Colourways	*Backstamp*	*U.S. $*	*Can. $*	*U.K. £*
Red/white/black	Puce	1,250.00	1,500.00	750.00

Note: Available with or without a wooden plinth.

RW3168
BENGAL LANCER

Modeller: Geraldine Blake
Height: 8 ½", 21.6 cm
Colour: Rider: Blue tunic and leggings; brown sash and belt; white turban with blue stripes
Horse: Brown
Issued: 1936-c.1950s

			Price	
Colourways	*Backstamp*	*U.S. $*	*Can. $*	*U.K. £*
Blue/brown	Puce	1,250.00	1,500.00	750.00

Note: Available with or without a wooden plinth.

RW3169
YOUNG ENTRY

Modeller: Geraldine Blake
Height: 7", 17.8 cm
Colour: Rider: Dark yellow habit; black riding hat
Horse: White with brown patches
Issued: 1936-c.1950s

	Price		
Backstamp	*U.S. $*	*Can. $*	*U.K. £*
1. Puce	1,250.00	1,500.00	750.00
2. Black	1,000.00	1,250.00	600.00

Note: Available with or without a wooden plinth.

RW3170
MARE AND FOAL

Modeller: Geraldine Blake
Height: 8 ½", 21.6 cm
Colour: Mare: Dark brown
Foal: Light brown
Issued: 1936-c.1950s

	Price		
Backstamp	*U.S. $*	*Can. $*	*U.K. £*
1. Puce	1,000.00	1,350.00	700.00
2. Black	900.00	1,250.00	600.00

Note: Available with or without a wooden plinth.

RW3179
CIRCUS HORSES (Three)

Modeller: Doris Lindner
Height: Without plinth: 10 ¾", 27.8 cm
With plinth: 14 ¾", 37.5 cm
Colour: Grey horses; red reins and breastplates
Plinth: Wooden
Issued: 1936-c.1970s

	Price		
Backstamp	*U.S. $*	*Can. $*	*U.K. £*
1. Puce	4,000.00	5,000.00	2,000.00
2. Black	3,500.00	4,250.00	1,750.00

RW3180
IN THE RING

Modeller: Doris Lindner
Height: Without plinth: 10 ¼", 26.0 cm
With plinth: 14 ¾", 37.5 cm
Colour: Rider: Yellow dress with red stars and white trim; white and yellow plume
Horses: Grey; red reins
Issued: 1936-c.1970

Backstamp	*U.S. $*	*Price Can. $*	*U.K. £*
1. Puce	6,000.00	7,500.00	3,000.00
2. Black	4,000.00	5,000.00	2,000.00

RW3184
POLAR BEAR ASHTRAY (Bear seated, looking up)

Modeller: Doris Lindner
Size: 7" x 5", 17.8 x 12.7 cm
Colour: White with grey shading
Issued: 1937-c.1940s
Varieties: Polar Bear Bookend (Bear seated, looking up) RW3063

Colourways	*Backstamp*	*U.S. $*	*Price Can. $*	*U.K. £*
White/grey shading	Puce	450.00	600.00	300.00

RW3185
POLAR BEAR ASHTRAY (Bear bending)

Modeller: Doris Lindner
Size: 6" x 3 ¾", 15.0 x 9.5 cm
Colour: White with grey shading
Issued: 1937-c.1940s
Varieties: Polar Bear Bookend (Bear bending) RW3062

Colourways	*Backstamp*	*U.S. $*	*Price Can. $*	*U.K. £*
White/grey shading	Puce	450.00	600.00	300.00

RW3187
FOAL

Modeller: Geraldine Blake
Height: 7 ¾", 19.7 cm
Colour: Brown with white markings; turquoise base
Issued: 1937-c.1950s

Backstamp	*U.S. $*	*Price* *Can. $*	*U.K. £*
1. Puce	700.00	1,000.00	500.00
2. Black	575.00	800.00	400.00

Note: Available with or without a wooden plinth.
The foal from model RW3170 was used to make model RW3187.

RW3188
FOXHOUND CALENDAR WITH FITTINGS

Modeller: Doris Lindner
Height: 4 ¾", 12.1 cm
Colour: 1. Coloured
2. White
Issued: 1937

Colourways	*Backstamp*	*U.S. $*	*Price* *Can. $*	*U.K. £*
1. Coloured	Puce	325.00	450.00	225.00
2. White	Green	275.00	400.00	200.00

RW3190
VIRGINIA CARDINAL AND ORANGE BLOSSOM (Cock)
(Richmondena Cardinalis)

Modeller: Dorothy Doughty
Height: 11 ½", 29.2 cm
Colour: Red with brown shading; pink flowers and buds; green leaves; brown branch
Plinth: Wooden
Issued: 1937 in a limited edition of 500
Series: Doughty American Birds

Colourways	*Backstamp*	*U.S. $*	*Price* *Can. $*	*U.K. £*
Red/brown/pink/green	Black	1,100.00	1,500.00	750.00

Note: Commissioned by Alex Dickens, USA.

RW3191
VIRGINIA CARDINAL AND ORANGE BLOSSOM (Hen)
(Richmondena Cardinalis)

Modeller:	Dorothy Doughty
Height:	11 ½", 29.2 cm
Colour:	Red with brown shading; pink flowers; green leaves; brown branch
Plinth:	Wooden
Issued:	1937 in a limited edition of 500
Series:	Doughty American Birds

			Price	
Colourways	*Backstamp*	*U.S. $*	*Can. $*	*U.K. £*
Red/brown/pink/green	Black	1,100.00	1,500.00	750.00

Note: Commissioned by Alex Dickens, USA.

RW3197
ROBIN

Modeller:	Eva Soper
Height:	2 ¾", 7.0 cm
Colour:	Red breast, brown feathers; red berries; green holly leaves; gloss or matt
Issued:	1937-1986
Series:	British Birds, Series One

			Price	
Description	*Backstamp*	*U.S. $*	*Can. $*	*U.K. £*
1. Gloss	Black	90.00	125.00	65.00
2. Matt	Black	70.00	100.00	50.00

RW3198
WREN

Modeller:	Eva Soper
Height:	2 ¼", 5.7 cm
Colour:	Browns and green; gloss or matt
Issued:	1937-1986
Series:	British Birds, Series One

			Price	
Description	*Backstamp*	*U.S. $*	*Can. $*	*U.K. £*
1. Gloss	Black	90.00	125.00	65.00
2. Matt	Black	70.00	100.00	50.00

RW3199
BLUE TIT

Modeller: Eva Soper
Height: 2 ¼", 5.7 cm
Colour: Light brown, blue, and cream; gloss or matt
Issued: 1937-1986
Series: British Birds, Series One

Description	*Backstamp*	*Price* *U.S. $*	*Can. $*	*U.K. £*
1. Gloss	Black	90.00	125.00	65.00
2. Matt	Black	70.00	100.00	50.00

RW3200
WOOD WARBLER

Modeller: Eva Soper
Height: 2 ¾", 7.0 cm
Colour: Yellow with green markings; pink base; gloss or matt
Issued: 1937-1986
Series: British Birds, Series One

Description	*Backstamp*	*Price* *U.S. $*	*Can. $*	*U.K. £*
1. Gloss	Black	90.00	125.00	65.00
2. Matt	Black	70.00	100.00	50.00

RW3223
INDIGO BUNTING ON PLUM TREE (Single)
(Passerina Cyanea)

Modeller: Dorothy Doughty
Height: 9 ½", 24.0 cm
Colour: Blue and turquoise bird; green leaves; brown branch
Plinth: Wooden
Issued: 1937 in a limited edition of 6
Series: Doughty American Birds

Colourways	*Backstamp*	*Price* *U.S. $*	*Can. $*	*U.K. £*
Blue/turquoise/green/brown	Black	750.00	1,000.00	500.00

Note: Commissioned by Alex Dickens, USA.

RW3228
IRISH SETTER / RED SETTER (With base)

Modeller: Doris Lindner
Height: 4 ½", 11.9 cm
Colour: 1. Irish Setter: Chocolate brown dog; green-brown base
2. Irish Setter: Chocolate brown dog; gold line around base
3. Red Setter: Red-brown; green base
4. Red Setter: Red-brown; gold line around base
Issued: 1. 1938-c.1955 3. 1938-c.1955
2. 1976-1980 4. 1976-1980
Varieties: Red Setter (Without base) RW3307
Series: Sporting Dogs

Description	*Backstamp*	*U.S. $*	*Price* *Can. $*	*U.K. £*
1. Irish Setter/green base	Black	475.00	500.00	225.00
2. Irish Setter/gold line	Black	450.00	450.00	200.00
3. Red Setter/green base	Black	475.00	500.00	225.00
4. Red Setter/ gold line	Black	450.00	450.00	200.00

RW3229
ENGLISH POINTER (With base)

Modeller: Doris Lindner
Height: 4 ½", 11.9 cm
Colour: 1. White with dark brown markings; green-brown base
2. White with dark brown markings; gold line around base
Issued: 1. 1938-c.1955
2. 1976-1980
Varieties: English Pointer (Without base) RW3308
Series: Sporting Dogs

Colourways	*Backstamp*	*U.S. $*	*Price* *Can. $*	*U.K. £*
1. White/brown/green base	Black	475.00	500.00	225.00
2. White/brown/gold line	Black	450.00	450.00	200.00

RW3230
GOLDEN RETRIEVER (With base)

Modeller: Doris Lindner
Height: 4 ½", 11.9 cm
Colour: 1. Golden brown; blue-green base
2. Golden brown; gold line around base
Issued: 1. 1938-c.1950s
2. 1976-1980
Varieties: Golden Retriever (Without base) RW3309
Series: Sporting Dogs

Colourways	*Backstamp*	*U.S. $*	*Price* *Can. $*	*U.K. £*
1. Golden brown/blue-green base	Black	475.00	500.00	225.00
2. Golden brown/gold line	Black	450.00	450.00	200.00

RW3231
COCKER SPANIEL (With base)

Modeller: Doris Lindner
Height: 4 ½", 11.9 cm
Colour: 1. Black and white dog; fawn rabbit; green base
2. Black and white dog; fawn rabbit; gold line around base
3. Blue roan dog; fawn rabbit; green-brown base
4. Blue roan dog; fawn rabbit; gold line around base
Issued: 1. 1938-c.1955 3. 1938-c.1955
2. 1976-1980 4. 1976-1980
Varieties: Cocker Spaniel (Without base) RW3310
Series: Sporting Dogs

Colourways	*Backstamp*	*U.S. $*	*Price Can. $*	*U.K. £*
1. Black/white/green base	Black	475.00	500.00	225.00
2. Black/white/gold line	Black	450.00	450.00	200.00
3. Blue roan/green-brown base	Black	475.00	500.00	225.00
4. Blue roan/gold line	Black	450.00	450.00	200.00

RW3232
CLUMBER SPANIEL / ENGLISH SPRINGER SPANIEL (With base)

Modeller: Doris Lindner
Height: 4 ½", 11.9 cm
Colour: 1. Grey-blue and white spaniel; green, red and yellow fowl
2. Grey-blue and white spaniel; gold line around base
3. Liver and white spaniel; green, red and yellow fowl
4. Liver and white spaniel; gold line around base
Issued: 1. 1938-c.1955 3. 1938-c.1955
2. 1976-1980 4. 1976-1980
Varieties: Clumber Spaniel (Without base) RW3311
Series: Sporting Dogs

Description	*Backstamp*	*U.S. $*	*Price Can. $*	*U.K. £*
1. Clumber Spaniel	Black	475.00	500.00	225.00
2. Clumber Spaniel/gold line	Black	450.00	450.00	200.00
3. Springer Spaniel	Black	475.00	500.00	225.00
4. Springer Spaniel/gold line	Black	450.00	450.00	200.00

RW3233
LABRADOR RETRIEVER (With base)

Modeller: Doris Lindner
Height: 4 ½", 11.9 cm
Colour: 1. Black
2. Black; gold line around base
3. Golden
4. Golden; gold line around base
Issued: 1. 1938-c.1955 3. 1938-c.1955
2. 1976-1980 4. 1976-1980
Varieties: Labrador Retriever (Without base) RW3312
Series: Sporting Dogs

Colourways	*Backstamp*	*U.S. $*	*Price Can. $*	*U.K. £*
1. Black	Black	475.00	500.00	225.00
2. Black/gold line	Black	450.00	450.00	200.00
3. Golden	Black	475.00	500.00	225.00
4. Golden/gold line	Black	450.00	450.00	200.00

RW3234
THRUSH
Style One

Modeller:	Eva Soper
Height:	4 ¾", 12.1 cm
Colour:	Light and dark brown thrush; red berries and orange leaves on base; gloss or matt
Issued:	1938-1986
Series:	British Birds, Series One

Description	*Backstamp*	*U.S. $*	*Price* *Can. $*	*U.K. £*
1. Gloss	Black	125.00	175.00	95.00
2. Matt	Black	110.00	150.00	80.00

RW3235
KINGFISHER

Modeller:	Eva Soper
Height:	3 ¼", 8.3 cm
Colour:	Blue and orange-browns; gloss or matt
Issued:	1938-1986
Series:	British Birds, Series One

Description	*Backstamp*	*U.S. $*	*Price* *Can. $*	*U.K. £*
1. Gloss	Puce	175.00	250.00	125.00
2. Matt	Black	150.00	200.00	100.00

RW3236
SPARROW

Modeller:	Eva Soper
Height:	3 ½", 8.9 cm
Colour:	Brown and grey sparrow; green leaves and red berries on base; gloss or matt
Issued:	1938-1986
Series:	British Birds, Series One

Description	*Backstamp*	*U.S. $*	*Price* *Can. $*	*U.K. £*
1. Gloss	Black	90.00	125.00	65.00
2. Matt	Black	70.00	100.00	50.00

RW3238
BULLFINCH

Modeller: Eva Soper
Height: 3", 7.6 cm
Colour: Brown, black and grey finch; light green base; gloss or matt
Issued: 1938-1986
Series: British Birds, Series One

Description	*Backstamp*	*U.S. $*	*Price Can. $*	*U.K. £*
1. Gloss	Black	90.00	125.00	65.00
2. Matt	Black	70.00	100.00	50.00

RW3239
GOLDFINCH

Modeller: Eva Soper
Height: 2 ¼", 5.7 cm
Colour: Browns, red, yellow and white finch; beige, maroon and grey base; gloss or matt
Issued: 1938-1986
Series: British Birds, Series One

Description	*Backstamp*	*U.S. $*	*Price Can. $*	*U.K. £*
1. Gloss	Green	90.00	125.00	65.00
2. Matt	Green	70.00	100.00	50.00

RW3240
CHAFFINCH
Style One

Modeller: Eva Soper
Height: 3 ¼", 8.3 cm
Colour: Orange, grey and black finch; green leaves; gloss or matt
Issued: 1938-1986
Series: British Birds, Series One

Description	*Backstamp*	*U.S. $*	*Price Can. $*	*U.K. £*
1. Gloss	Black	90.00	125.00	65.00
2. Matt	Black	70.00	100.00	50.00

RW3241
CHICKADEE AND LARCH (Cock)
(Parus Atricapillus)

Modeller:	Dorothy Doughty
Height:	9 ½", 24.0 cm
Colour:	Brown and grey bird; brown cones; green spikes; brown and grey branch
Plinth:	Wooden
Issued:	1938 in a limited edition of 325
Series:	Doughty American Birds

Colourways	*Backstamp*	*U.S. $*	*Price Can. $*	*U.K. £*
Brown/grey/green	Black	750.00	1,000.00	500.00

Note: Commissioned by Alex Dickens, USA.

RW3242
CHICKADEE AND LARCH (Hen)
(Parus Atricapillus)

Modeller:	Dorothy Doughty
Height:	9 ½", 24.0 cm
Colour:	Brown and grey bird; brown cones; green spikes; brown and grey branch
Plinth:	Wooden
Issued:	1938 in a limited edition of 325
Series:	Doughty American Birds

Colourways	*Backstamp*	*U.S. $*	*Price Can. $*	*U.K. £*
Brown/grey/green	Black	750.00	1,000.00	500.00

Note: Commissioned by Alex Dickens, USA.

RW3243
WELSH CORGI

Modeller:	Doris Lindner
Height:	2", 5.0 cm
Colour:	Red-brown and cream
Issued:	1938-c.1950s
Series:	Small Dogs

Colourways	*Backstamp*	*U.S. $*	*Price Can. $*	*U.K. £*
Red-brown	Black	300.00	325.00	125.00

RW3248
JAY

Modeller: Eva Soper
Height: 6 ¼", 15.9 cm
Colour: Orange-brown with blue highlights; light green and beige base; gloss or matt
Issued: 1938-1986
Series: British Birds, Series One

Description	*Backstamp*	*U.S. $*	*Price* *Can. $*	*U.K. £*
1. Gloss	Black	350.00	500.00	250.00
2. Matt	Black	300.00	450.00	225.00

RW3249
WOODPECKER

Modeller: Eva Soper
Height: 7 ¼", 18.4 cm
Colour: Light yellow, green, black and dark red; mauve and light brown base; gloss or matt
Issued: 1938-1986
Series: British Birds, Series One

Description	*Backstamp*	*U.S. $*	*Price* *Can. $*	*U.K. £*
1. Gloss	Black	350.00	500.00	250.00
2. Matt	Black	300.00	450.00	225.00

RW3263
LEOPARDS, NELSON AND NORAH (With base)

Modeller: Doris Lindner
Height: 3 ½", 8.9 cm
Colour: Light tan with spot; light green base
Issued: 1938-by 1953
Varieties: Leopards, Nelson and Norah (Without base) RW3313
Series: Zoo Babies

Colourways	*Backstamp*	*U.S. $*	*Price* *Can. $*	*U.K. £*
Light tan	Black	900.00	1,250.00	650.00

See page 69
for this model
without a base

See page 70
for this model
without a base

RW3264
LIONS, OLIVER AND OCTOBER (With base)

Modeller: Doris Lindner
Height: 3 ½", 8.9 cm
Colour: Light brown; light green base
Issued: 1938-by 1953
Varieties: Lions, Oliver and October (Without base) RW3314
Series: Zoo Babies

Colourways	*Backstamp*	*Price* *U.S. $*	*Can. $*	*U.K. £*
Light brown	Black	950.00	1,400.00	700.00

RW3265
BEARS, MICK AND MACK (With base)

Modeller: Doris Lindner
Height: 4 ¼", 10.8 cm
Colour: Brown; light green base
Issued: 1938-by 1953
Varieties: Bears, Mick and Mack (Without base) RW3315
Series: Zoo Babies

Colourways	*Backstamp*	*Price* *U.S. $*	*Can. $*	*U.K. £*
Brown	Black	1,500.00	1,850.00	950.00

RW3266
FAWNS, YOUNG SPOTTED DEER (Rectangular base)

Modeller: Doris Lindner
Height: 4 ¾", 12.1 cm
Colour: Brown with white markings
Issued: 1938
Varieties: Fawns, Young Spotted Deer (Oval base) RW3316;
Fawns, Young Spotted Deer (Without base) RW3529
Series: Zoo Babies

Colourways	*Backstamp*	*Price* *U.S. $*	*Can. $*	*U.K. £*
Brown/white	Black	600.00	900.00	450.00

RW3268
BALTIMORE ORIOLE AND TULIP TREE (Cock)
(Icterus Galbula)

Modeller:	Dorothy Doughty
Height:	9 ½", 24.0 cm
Colour:	1. Dark brown, red and yellow bird; yellow flowers; green leaves 2. White
Plinth:	Wooden
Issued:	1. Coloured: 1938 in a limited edition of 250 2. White: 1938 in a limited edition of 250
Series:	Doughty American Birds

Colourways	*Backstamp*	*U.S. $*	*Price* *Can. $*	*U.K. £*
1. Coloured (as above)	Black	1,000.00	1,500.00	700.00
2. White	Black	275.00	400.00	200.00

Note: Commissioned by Alex Dickens, USA.

RW3269
BALTIMORE ORIOLE AND TULIP TREE (Hen)
(Icterus Galbula)

Modeller:	Dorothy Doughty
Height:	9 ½", 24.0 cm
Colour:	1. Browns, red and yellow bird; yellow flowers; green leaves 2. White
Plinth:	Wooden
Issued:	1. Coloured: 1938 in a limited edition of 250 2. White: 1938 in a limited edition of 250
Series:	Doughty American Birds

Colourways	*Backstamp*	*U.S. $*	*Price* *Can. $*	*U.K. £*
1. Coloured (as above)	Black	1,000.00	1,500.00	700.00
2. White	Black	275.00	400.00	200.00

Note: Commissioned by Alex Dickens, USA.

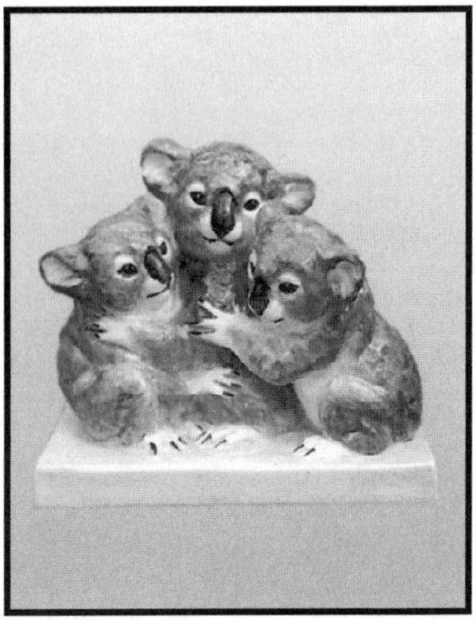

RW3273
KOALA BEARS, BILLY BLUEGUMS (With base)

Modeller:	Doris Lindner
Height:	4 ¾", 12.1 cm
Colour:	Pale blue and white; green or beige base
Issued:	1938-by 1953
Varieties:	Koala Bears, Billy Bluegums (Without base) RW3317
Series:	Zoo Babies

Colourways	*Backstamp*	*U.S. $*	*Price* *Can. $*	*U.K. £*
Grey-brown	Black	800.00	1,200.00	575.00

RW3274
TIGERS, MAURICE AND SONIA (With base)

Modeller: Doris Lindner
Height: 3 ½", 8.9 cm
Colour: Golden brown with darker brown markings
Issued: 1938-by 1953
Varieties: Tigers, Maurice and Sonia (Without base) RW3318
Series: Zoo Babies

Colourways	*Backstamp*	*Price* *U.S. $*	*Can. $*	*U.K. £*
Orange/brown/white	Black	850.00	1,250.00	600.00

RW3293
DALMATIAN

Modeller: Doris Lindner
Height: 3 ¼", 8.3 cm
Colour: 1. White with black spots
2. White
Issued: 1939-c.1950s
Series: Small Dogs

Colourways	*Backstamp*	*Price* *U.S. $*	*Can. $*	*U.K. £*
1. White/black	Black	300.00	350.00	175.00
2. White	Green	150.00	200.00	100.00

RW3294
DACHSHUND

Modeller: Doris Lindner
Height: 2 ½", 6.4 cm
Colour: 1. Dark brown with golden brown underbody
2. Golden brown
3. White
Issued: 1939-c.1950s
Series: Small Dogs

Colourways	*Backstamp*	*Price* *U.S. $*	*Can. $*	*U.K. £*
1. Coloured (as above)	Black	225.00	300.00	150.00
2. White	Green	150.00	200.00	100.00

RW3295
ALSATIAN
Style One

Modeller: Doris Lindner
Height: 3 ½", 8.9 cm
Colour: Light brown with black shading
Issued: 1939-c.1950s
Series: Small Dogs

Colourways	*Backstamp*	*U.S. $*	*Price Can. $*	*U.K. £*
Light brown/black	Black	275.00	350.00	175.00

RW3296
HACKING IN THE PARK

Modeller: Doris Lindner
Height: 6 ¾", 17.2 cm
Colour: Rider: Light brown jacket; white jodhpurs; black boots
Horse: Brown; tan saddle
Plinth: Wooden
Issued: 1939-by 1970

Backstamp	*U.S. $*	*Price Can. $*	*U.K. £*
1. Puce	1,500.00	1,850.00	900.00
2. Black	800.00	1,000.00	400.00

RW3307
RED SETTER (Without base)

Modeller: Doris Lindner
Size: 7" x 4 ¼", 17.8 x 10.8 cm
Colour: Reddish-brown
Issued: 1940-c.1955
Varieties: Irish Setter /Red Setter (With base) RW3228
Series: Sporting Dogs

Colourways	*Backstamp*	*U.S. $*	*Price Can. $*	*U.K. £*
Reddish-brown	Green	375.00	450.00	225.00

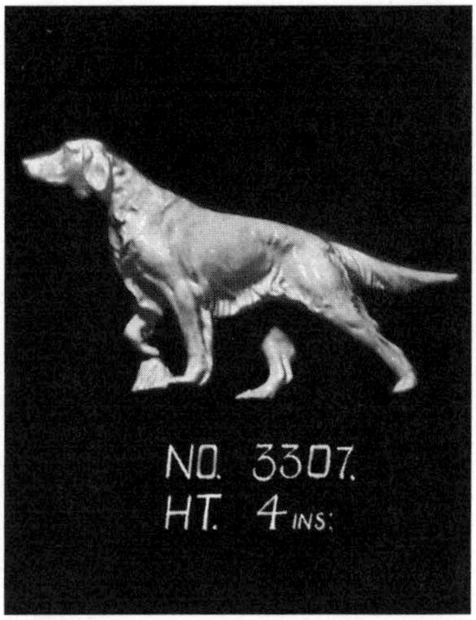

RW3308
ENGLISH POINTER (Without base)

Modeller: Doris Lindner
Height: 8″ x 4″, 20.3 x 10.1 cm
Colour: White with brown patches
Issued: 1940-c.1955
Varieties: English Pointer (With base) RW3229
Series: Sporting Dogs

Colourways	*Backstamp*	*U.S. $*	*Price* *Can. $*	*U.K. £*
White/brown	Green	375.00	450.00	225.00

RW3309
GOLDEN RETRIEVER (Without base)

Modeller: Doris Lindner
Size: 7 ½″ x 3 ½″, 19.1 x 8.9 cm
Colour: Golden brown
Issued: 1940-c.1955
Varieties: Golden Retriever (With base) RW3230
Series: Sporting Dogs

Colourways	*Backstamp*	*U.S. $*	*Price* *Can. $*	*U.K. £*
Golden brown	Green	375.00	450.00	225.00

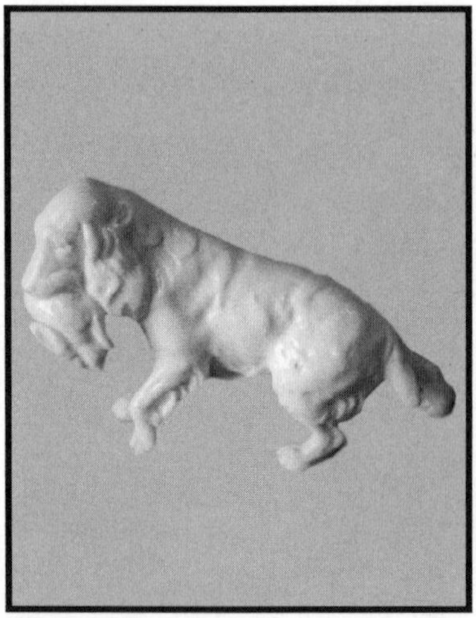

RW3310
COCKER SPANIEL (Without base)

Modeller: Doris Lindner
Size: 5 ½″ x 3 ¾″, 14.0 x 9.5 cm
Colour: White with black patches; brown rabbit
Issued: 1940-c.1955
Varieties: Cocker Spaniel (With base) RW3231
Series: Sporting Dogs

Colourways	*Backstamp*	*U.S. $*	*Price* *Can. $*	*U.K. £*
White/black	Green	375.00	450.00	225.00

RW3311
CLUMBER SPANIEL (Without base)

Modeller: Doris Lindner
Height: 6" x 4", 15.0 x 10.1 cm
Colour: White with brown patches
Issued: 1940-c.1955
Varieties: Clummer Spaniel (With base) / English Springer Spaniel (With base) RW3232
Series: Sporting Dogs

Colourways	*Backstamp*	*U.S. $*	*Price Can. $*	*U.K. £*
White/brown	Green	375.00	450.00	225.00

RW3312
LABRADOR RETRIEVER (Without base)

Modeller: Doris Lindner
Height: 3 ¾", 9.5 cm
Colour: Black
Issued: 1940-c.1955
Varieties: Labrador Retreiver (With base) RW3233
Series: Sporting Dogs

Colourways	*Backstamp*	*U.S. $*	*Price Can. $*	*U.K. £*
Black	Black	375.00	450.00	225.00

RW3313
LEOPARDS, NELSON AND NORAH (Without base)

Modeller: Doris Lindner
Height: 3 ½", 8.9 cm
Colour: Golden brown, brown spots
Issued: 1940
Varieties: Leopards, Nelson and Norah (With base) RW3263
Series: Zoo Babies

Colourways	*Backstamp*	*U.S. $*	*Price Can. $*	*U.K. £*
Golden brown	Puce	900.00	1,250.00	650.00

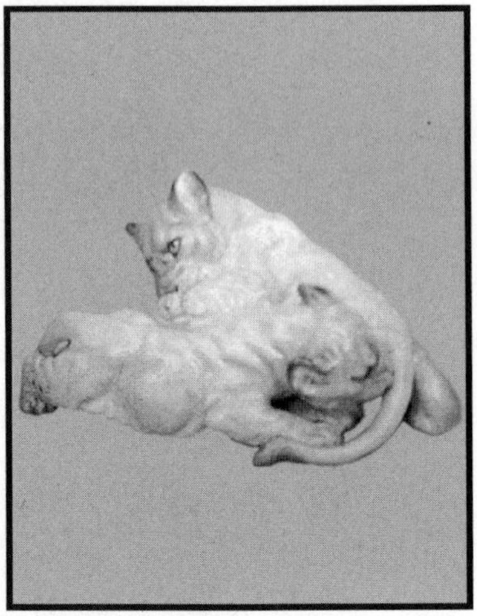

RW3314
LIONS, OLIVER AND OCTOBER (Without base)

Modeller: Doris Lindner
Height: 3 ¼", 8.3 cm
Colour: Golden brown
Issued: 1940
Varieties: Lions, Oliver and October (With base) RW3264
Series: Zoo Babies

Colourways	*Backstamp*	*Price U.S. $*	*Can. $*	*U.K. £*
Golden	Black	950.00	1,400.00	700.00

RW3315
BEARS, MICK AND MACK (Without base)

Modeller: Doris Lindner
Height: 3 ½", 8.9 cm
Colour: Dark brown
Issued: 1940
Varieties: Bears, Mick and Mack (With base) RW3265
Series: Zoo Babies

Colourways	*Backstamp*	*Price U.S. $*	*Can. $*	*U.K. £*
Dark brown	Black	1,500.00	1,850.00	950.00

RW3316
FAWNS, YOUNG SPOTTED DEER (Oval base)

Modeller: Doris Lindner
Height: 4 ¾", 12.1 cm
Colour: Brown with white markings; light green oval base
Issued: 1940
Varieties: Fawns, Young Spotted Dear (Rectangular base) RW3266;
Fawns, Young Spotted Dear (Without base) RW3529
Series: Zoo Babies

Backstamp	*Price U.S. $*	*Can. $*	*U.K. £*
1. Green	600.00	900.00	450.00
2. Puce	600.00	900.00	450.00

RW3317
KOALA BEARS, BILLY BLUEGUMS (Without base)

Modeller: Doris Lindner
Height: 3 ½", 8.9 cm
Colour: Pale blue and white
Issued: 1940
Varieties: Koala Bears, Billy Bluegums (With base) RW3273
Series: Zoo Babies

			Price	
Colourways	*Backstamp*	*U.S. $*	*Can. $*	*U.K. £*
Pale blue/white	Black	800.00	1,200.00	575.00

RW3318
TIGERS, MAURICE AND SONIA (Without base)

Modeller: Doris Lindner
Height: 3 ½", 8.9 cm
Colour: Golden brown with darker brown markings
Issued: 1940
Varieties: Tigers, Maurice and Sonia (With base) RW3274
Series: Zoo Babies

			Price	
Colourways	*Backstamp*	*U.S. $*	*Can. $*	*U.K. £*
Golden brown	Black	850.00	1,250.00	600.00

RW3319
SCOTTISH TERRIER, DOG'S HEAD (Wall Mount)

Modeller: Doris Lindner
Height: 6", 15.0 cm
Colour: Black
Issued: 1940
Series: Wall Mounts

			Price	
Colourways	*Backstamp*	*U.S. $*	*Can. $*	*U.K. £*
Black	Black	1,000.00	1,000.00	300.00

RW3320
BULLDOG, DOG'S HEAD (Wall mount)

Modeller: Doris Lindner
Height: 6", 15.0 cm
Colour: Brown
Issued: 1940
Series: Wall Mounts

			Price	
Colourways	*Backstamp*	*U.S. $*	*Can. $*	*U.K. £*
Brown	Black	1,000.00	1,000.00	300.00

RW3321
SPANIEL, DOG'S HEAD (Wall mount)

Modeller: Doris Lindner
Height: 6", 15.0 cm
Colour: Brown and white
Issued: 1940
Series: Wall Mounts

			Price	
Colourways	*Backstamp*	*U.S. $*	*Can. $*	*U.K. £*
Brown/white	Black	1,000.00	1,000.00	300.00

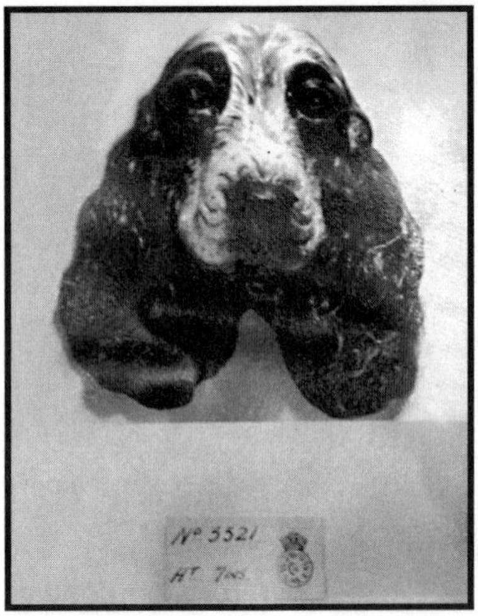

RW3322
PEKINESE, DOG'S HEAD (Wall mount)

Modeller: Doris Lindner
Height: 6", 15.0 cm
Colour: Brown
Issued: 1940
Series: Wall Mounts

			Price	
Colourways	*Backstamp*	*U.S. $*	*Can. $*	*U.K. £*
Brown	Black	1,000.00	1,000.00	300.00

RW3323
BOB-WHITE QUAIL (Cock)
(Colinus Virginianus)
Style One

Modeller: Dorothy Doughty
Height: 6", 15.0 cm
Colour: Reddish-brown, grey and mauve
Issued: 1940 in a limited edition of 22
Series: Doughty American Birds

Colourways	*Backstamp*	*U.S. $*	*Price Can. $*	*U.K. £*
Reddish-brown/grey/mauve	Black	1,200.00	1,750.00	850.00

Note: Commissioned by Alex Dickens, USA.

RW3324
BOB-WHITE QUAIL (Hen)
(Colinus Virginianus)
Style One

Modeller: Dorothy Doughty
Height: 6", 15.0 cm
Colour: Reddish-brown, grey and mauve hen with two chicks
Issued: 1940 in a limited edition of 22
Series: Doughty American Birds

Colourways	*Backstamp*	*U.S. $*	*Price Can. $*	*U.K. £*
Reddish-brown/grey/mauve	Black	1,200.00	1,750.00	850.00

Note: Commissioned by Alex Dickens, USA.

RW3326
MOCKINGBIRD AND PEACH BLOSSOM (Cock)
(Mimus Polyglottos)

Modeller: Dorothy Doughty
Height: 10 ½", 26.7 cm
Colour: Blue-grey, yellow, brown and white bird; pink blossom; green-brown leaves
Plinth: Wooden
Issued: 1940 in a limited edition of 500
Series: Doughty American Birds

Colourways	*Backstamp*	*U.S. $*	*Price Can. $*	*U.K. £*
Blue-grey/yellow/brown	Black	1,000.00	1,500.00	750.00

Note: Commissioned by Alex Dickens, USA.

RW3327
MOCKINGBIRD AND PEACH BLOSSOM (Hen)
(Mimus Polyglottos)

Modeller:	Dorothy Doughty
Height:	10 ½", 26.7 cm
Colour:	Blue-grey, yellow, brown and white bird; pink blossom; green-brown leaves
Plinth:	Wooden
Issued:	1940 in a limited edition of 500
Series:	Doughty American Birds

			Price	
Colourways	*Backstamp*	*U.S. $*	*Can. $*	*U.K. £*
Blue-grey/brown/white	Black	1,000.00	1,500.00	750.00

Note: Commissioned by Alex Dickens, USA.

RW3328
CRAB APPLE SPRAYS AND ONE BUTTERFLY

Modeller:	Dorothy Doughty
Height:	10", 25.4 cm
Colour:	Pink and white blossom; green leaves; brown branch; one blue butterfly
Plinth:	Wooden
Issued:	1940 in a limited edition of 250

			Price	
Colourways	*Backstamp*	*U.S. $*	*Can. $*	*U.K. £*
Pink/white/green/brown/blue	Black	500.00	750.00	350.00

RW3329
CRAB APPLE SPRAYS AND TWO BUTTERFLIES

Modeller:	Dorothy Doughty
Height:	10", 25.4 cm
Colour:	Pink and white blossom; green leaves; brown branch; two blue butterflies
Plinth:	Wooden
Issued:	1940 in a limited edition of 250

			Price	
Colourways	*Backstamp*	*U.S. $*	*Can. $*	*U.K. £*
Pink/white/green/brown/blue	Black	500.00	750.00	350.00

RW3330
BOGSKAR

Modeller: Doris Lindner
Height: 9", 22.9 cm
Colour: 1. Rider: Blue and gold silks; white jodhpurs
Horse: Brown
2. White
Issued: 1940-by 1942

Colourways	*Backstamp*	*U.S. $*	*Price* *Can. $*	*U.K. £*
1. Coloured (as above)	Puce		Rare	
2. White	Green		Rare	

Note: "Bogskar," owned by Lord Stalbridge, was the Grand National winner in 1940.

RW3331
CAIRN TERRIER "TOTO"

Modeller: Aline Ellis
Height: 3 ½", 8.9 cm
Colour: Black; red tongue; yellow brick road base
Issued: 1940

Colourways	*Backstamp*	*U.S. $*	*Price* *Can. $*	*U.K. £*
Black/yellow	Black	750.00	1,000.00	375.00

Note: Commissioned by Alex Dickens and made exclusively for the USA market.

RW3333
HEDGE SPARROW

Modeller: Eva Soper
Height: 2 ½", 6.4 cm
Colour: Red with brown markings; gloss or matt
Issued: 1941-1986
Series: British Birds, Series One

Description	*Backstamp*	*U.S. $*	*Price* *Can. $*	*U.K. £*
1. Gloss	Black	90.00	125.00	65.00
2. Matt	Black	70.00	100.00	50.00

RW3334
NUTHATCH

Modeller: Eva Soper
Height: 2 ½", 6.4 cm
Colour: Red, black and yellow; gloss or matt
Issued: 1941-1986
Series: British Birds, Series One

Description	*Backstamp*	*U.S. $*	*Price* *Can. $*	*U.K. £*
1. Gloss	Black	90.00	125.00	65.00
2. Matt	Black	70.00	100.00	50.00

RW3335
GREAT TIT

Modeller: Eva Soper
Height: 2 ½", 6.4 cm
Colour: Grey, yellow and green; gloss or matt
Issued: 1941-1986
Series: British Birds, Series One

Description	*Backstamp*	*U.S. $*	*Price* *Can. $*	*U.K. £*
1. Gloss	Black	90.00	125.00	65.00
2. Matt	Black	70.00	100.00	50.00

RW3336
MARSH TIT
Style One

Modeller: Eva Soper
Height: 2 ¼", 5.7 cm
Colour: Black and yellow; gloss or matt
Issued: 1941-1986
Series: British Birds, Series One

Description	*Backstamp*	*U.S. $*	*Price* *Can. $*	*U.K. £*
1. Gloss	Black	95.00	125.00	65.00
2. Matt	Black	75.00	100.00	50.00

RW3337
NIGHTINGALE

Modeller: Eva Soper
Height: 3 ½", 8.9 cm
Colour: Orangey-brown and cream; green leaf base; gloss or matt
Issued: 1941-1986
Series: British Birds, Series One

Description	*Backstamp*	*U.S. $*	*Price Can. $*	*U.K. £*
1. Gloss	Black	110.00	150.00	80.00
2. Matt	Black	95.00	125.00	65.00

RW3338
GOLDCREST

Modeller: Eva Soper
Height: 2 ¼", 5.7 cm
Colour: Browns and greys; gloss or matt
Issued: 1941-1986
Series: British Birds, Series One

Description	*Backstamp*	*U.S. $*	*Price Can. $*	*U.K. £*
1. Gloss	Black	110.00	150.00	80.00
2. Matt	Black	95.00	125.00	65.00

RW3350
CAIRN TERRIER "RATS"

Modeller: Aline Ellis
Height: 3 ¼", 8.3 cm
Colour: Light beige terrier; green base "Rats"
Issued: 1941

Colourways	*Backstamp*	*U.S. $*	*Price Can. $*	*U.K. £*
Light beige/green	Black	500.00	750.00	350.00

Note: Commissioned by Alex Dickens and made exclusively for the USA market.

RW3355
WEST HIGHLAND TERRIER "MACK"

Modeller: Aline Ellis
Height: 3", 7.6 cm
Colour: Creamy-brown terrier; green base
Issued: 1941

Colourways	Backstamp	U.S. $	Price Can. $	U.K. £
Creamy-brown	Black	500.00	750.00	300.00

Note: Commissioned by Alex Dickens and made exclusively for the USA market.

RW3356
HOUND "RANTER"

Modeller: Aline Ellis
Height: 4", 10.1 cm
Colour: White with reddish-brown, brown and black patches; green-brown base "Ranter"
Issued: 1941

Colourways	Backstamp	U.S. $	Price Can. $	U.K. £
White with patches	Black	600.00	750.00	300.00

Note: Commissioned by Alex Dickens and made exclusively for the USA market.

RW3357
APPLE BLOSSOM SPRAY AND ONE BEE

Modeller: Dorothy Doughty
Height: 6 ½", 16.5 cm
Colour: Pink and white flowers; green leaves; one bee
Plinth: Wooden
Issued: 1941 in a limited edition of 250

Colourways	Backstamp	U.S. $	Price Can. $	U.K. £
Pink/white/green	Black	550.00	750.00	375.00

RW3358
APPLE BLOSSOM SPRAY AND TWO BEES

Modeller: Dorothy Doughty
Height: 4", 10.4 cm
Colour: Pink and white flowers; green leaves; two bees
Plinth: Wooden
Issued: 1941 in a limited edition of 250

			Price	
Colourways	*Backstamp*	*U.S. $*	*Can. $*	*U.K. £*
Pink/white/green	Black	550.00	750.00	375.00

RW3361
SPANIEL PUPPY "TONY"

Modeller: Aline Ellis
Height: 3", 7.6 cm
Colour: Brown and white; green base "Tony"
Issued: 1941

			Price	
Colourways	*Backstamp*	*U.S. $*	*Can. $*	*U.K. £*
Brown/white	Puce	450.00	750.00	275.00

Note: Commissioned by Alex Dickens and made exclusively for the USA market.

RW3363
PIED WOODPECKERS (On stump)

Modeller: Eva Soper
Height: 4 ¾", 12.1 cm
Colour: Grey, white and black
Issued: 1942-1986
Series: Double Birds on Tree Stumps

			Price	
Colourways	*Backstamp*	*U.S. $*	*Can. $*	*U.K. £*
Grey/white/black	Black	250.00	350.00	175.00

RW3364
CHAFFINCHES (On stump)

Modeller: Eva Soper
Height: 5″, 12.7 cm
Colour: Browns, blue and white
Issued: 1942-1986
Series: Double Birds on Tree Stumps

Colourways	*Backstamp*	*U.S. $*	*Price Can. $*	*U.K. £*
Browns/blue/white	Black	200.00	300.00	150.00

RW3365
LINNETS (On stump)

Modeller: Eva Soper
Height: 4 ¾″, 12.1 cm
Colour: Reddish-brown, grey and yellow
Issued: 1942-1986
Series: Double Birds on Tree Stumps

Colourways	*Backstamp*	*U.S. $*	*Price Can. $*	*U.K. £*
Grey/reddish-brown	Black	200.00	300.00	150.00

RW3366
WELSH CORGI "TAFFY"

Modeller: Aline Ellis
Height: 3″, 7.6 cm
Colour: Reddish-brown and white; green base "Taffy"
Issued: 1941

Colourways	*Backstamp*	*U.S. $*	*Price Can. $*	*U.K. £*
Reddish-brown/white	Black	450.00	750.00	300.00

Note: Commissioned by Alex Dickens and made exclusively for the USA market.

AMERICAN BIRDS

BY DOROTHY DOUGHTY

RW3532 Ovenbird with Lady's Slipper (Cock)

RW3533 Ovenbird with Crested Iris (Hen)

RW3464 Yellow-Headed Blackbird and Spiderwort (Cock)

RW3465 Yellow-Headed Blackbird and Spiderwort (Hen)

RW3326 Mockingbird and Peach Blossom (Cock)

RW3327 Mockingbird and Peach Blossom (Hen)

RW3268 Baltimore Oriole and Tulip Tree (Cock)

RW3269 Baltimore Oriole and Tulip Tree (Hen)

RW3540 Yellow-Throat and Water Hyacinth (Hen)

RW3539 Yellow-Throat and Water Hyacinth (Cock)

RW3618 Cactus Wren and Prickly Pear (Cock)

RW3619 Cactus Wren and Prickly Pear (Hen)

RW3438 Ruby-Throated Hummingbird and Fuchsia (Cock)

RW3439 Ruby-Throated Hummingbird and Fuchsia (Hen)

RW3137 Bluebird and Apple Blossom (Cock)

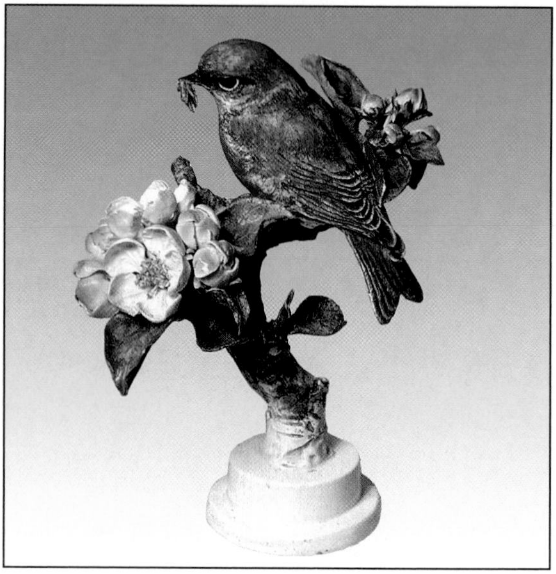

RW3136 Bluebird and Apple Blossom (Hen)

RW3651 Lazuli Bunting and Choke Cherry (Cock)

RW3652 Lazuli Bunting and Choke Cherry (Hen)

RW3658 Vermilion Flycatcher and Pussy Willow (Hen)

RW3657 Vermilion Flycatcher and Pussy Willow (Cock)

RW3591 Hooded Warbler and Cherokee Rose (Hen)

RW3590 Hooded Warbler and Cherokee Rose (Cock)

RW3191 Virginia Cardinal and Orange Blossom (Hen)

RW3190 Virginia Cardinal and Orange Blossom (Cock)

RW3512 Bewick's Wren and Yellow Jasmine (Cock)

RW3513 Bewick's Wren and Yellow Jasmine (Hen)

RW3469 Red-Eyed Vireo and Swamp Azalea (Cock)

RW3470 Red-Eyed Vireo and Swamp Azalea (Hen)

RW3536 Parula Warbler and Sweet Bay (Cock)

RW3537 Parula Warbler and Sweet Bay (Hen)

RW3429 Magnolia Warbler and Magnolia (Hen)

RW3430 Magnolia Warbler and Magnolia (Cock)

RW3367
INDIGO BUNTING AND BLACKBERRY (Cock)
(Passerina Cyanea)

Modeller:	Dorothy Doughty
Height:	8 ½", 21.6 cm
Colour:	Blue bird; red berries; white flowers; green leaves; brown branch
Plinth:	Wooden
Issued:	1941 in a limited edition of 500
Series:	Doughty American Birds

			Price	
Colourways	*Backstamp*	*U.S. $*	*Can. $*	*U.K. £*
Blue/red/white/green/brown	Black	750.00	1,000.00	500.00

Note: Commissioned by Alex Dickens, USA.

RW3368
INDIGO BUNTING AND BLACKBERRY (Hen)
(Passerina Cyanea)

Modeller:	Dorothy Doughty
Height:	8 ½", 21.6 cm
Colour:	Brown bird with red breast; dark blue blackberries; green leaves; brown branch
Plinth:	Wooden
Issued:	1941 in a limited edition of 500
Series:	Doughty American Birds

			Price	
Colourways	*Backstamp*	*U.S. $*	*Can. $*	*U.K. £*
Brown/red/dark blue/green	Black	750.00	1,000.00	500.00

Note: Commissioned by Alex Dickens, USA.

RW3375
BLUE TITS (On stump)

Modeller:	Eva Soper
Height:	4 ¾", 12.1 cm
Colour:	Blue and yellow
Issued:	1942-1986
Series:	Double Birds on Tree Stumps

			Price	
Colourways	*Backstamp*	*U.S. $*	*Can. $*	*U.K. £*
Blue/yellow	Black	200.00	300.00	150.00

RW3376
COLE TITS (On stump)

Modeller: Eva Soper
Height: 4 ¾", 12.1 cm
Colour: Light browns, yellow and black
Issued: 1942-1986
Series: Double Birds on Tree Stumps

Colourways	*Backstamp*	*U.S. $*	*Price Can. $*	*U.K. £*
Brown/yellow/black	Black	225.00	325.00	160.00

RW3377
YELLOWHAMMERS (On stump)

Modeller: Eva Soper
Height: 4 ¾", 12.1 cm
Colour: Yellow and light browns
Issued: 1942-1986
Series: Double Birds on Tree Stumps

Colourways	*Backstamp*	*U.S. $*	*Price Can. $*	*U.K. £*
Yellow/light browns	Black	225.00	325.00	160.00

RW3378
ORANGE BLOSSOM SPRAY AND BUTTERFLY

Modeller: Dorothy Doughty
Height: 7 ¼", 18.4 cm
Colour: White flowers with yellow centres; green leaves; brown and gold butterfly
Plinth: Wooden
Issued: 1947 in a limited edition of 175

Colourways	*Backstamp*	*U.S. $*	*Price Can. $*	*U.K. £*
White/yellow/green	Black	350.00	500.00	250.00

RW3379
ORANGE BLOSSOM SPRAY

Modeller: Dorothy Doughty
Height: 7 ¼", 18.4 cm
Colour: White flowers with yellow centres; green leaves
Plinth: Wooden
Issued: 1947 in a limited edition of 175

Colourways	*Backstamp*	*U.S. $*	*Price* *Can. $*	*U.K. £*
White/yellow/green	Black	350.00	500.00	250.00

RW3385
FOXHOUND (Standing)
Style One

Modeller: Aline Ellis
Height: 7", 17.8 cm
Colour: White with red-brown patches; matt
Issued: 1942

Colourways	*Backstamp*	*U.S. $*	*Price* *Can. $*	*U.K. £*
White/red-brown	Puce	700.00	875.00	350.00

Note: Commissioned by Alex Dickens and made exclusively for the USA market.

RW3386
FOXHOUND (Standing)
Style Two

Modeller: Aline Ellis
Height: 7", 17.8 cm
Colour: White with red-brown patches; green base
Issued: 1942

Colourways	*Backstamp*	*U.S. $*	*Price* *Can. $*	*U.K. £*
White/red-brown	Black	700.00	875.00	350.00

Photograph not available at press time

RW3387
FOX
Style One

Modeller: Aline Ellis
Height: 5″, 12.7 cm
Colour: Red-brown; black paws, markings; light green base
Issued: 1942-by1948

Colourways	*Backstamp*	*U.S. $*	*Price Can. $*	*U.K. £*
Red-brown	Black	500.00	750.00	375.00

RW3421
WOOD PIGEON
Style One

Modeller: Doris Lindner
Height: 7″, 17.8 cm
Colour: Naturalistically coloured
Issued: 1947

Colourways	*Backstamp*	*U.S. $*	*Price Can. $*	*U.K. £*
Natural	Black	650.00	950.00	475.00

Photograph not available at press time

Photograph not available at press time

RW3422
WOOD PIGEON
Style Two

Modeller: Doris Lindner
Height: 7″, 17.8 cm
Colour: Naturalistically coloured
Issued: 1947

Colourways	*Backstamp*	*U.S. $*	*Price Can. $*	*U.K. £*
Natural	Black	650.00	950.00	475.00

RW3425
AFGHANISTAN HOUND

Modeller: Doris Lindner
Height: 8", 20.3 cm
Colour: 1. Naturalistically coloured
2. White
Issued: 1947-c.1958
Series: Large Dogs

		Price		
Colourways	*Backstamp*	*U.S. $*	*Can. $*	*U.K. £*
1. Natural	Black	1,200.00	1,500.00	500.00
2. White	Green	1,000.00	1,250.00	400.00

RW3426
BORZOI
Style One

Modeller: Doris Lindner
Height: 8", 20.3 cm
Colour: 1. Naturalistically coloured
2. White
Issued: 1947-c.1958
Series: Large Dogs

		Price		
Colourways	*Backstamp*	*U.S. $*	*Can. $*	*U.K. £*
1. Natural	Black	1,200.00	1,500.00	500.00
2. White	Green	1,000.00	1,250.00	400.00

RW3429
MAGNOLIA WARBLER AND MAGNOLIA (Hen)
(Dendroica Magnolia)

Modeller: Dorothy Doughty
Height: 14 ¾", 37.5 cm
Colour: Green, yellow and brown bird; white flower; green leaves
Plinth: Wooden
Issued: 1950 in a limited edition of 150
Series: Doughty American Birds

		Price		
Colourways	*Backstamp*	*U.S. $*	*Can. $*	*U.K. £*
Green/yellow/brown/white	Black	1,250.00	1,750.00	900.00

RW3430
MAGNOLIA WARBLER AND MAGNOLIA (Cock)
(Dendroica Magnolia)

Modeller:	Dorothy Doughty
Height:	14 ¾", 37.5 cm
Colour:	Dark grey and yellow bird; white flower; green leaves
Plinth:	Wooden
Issued:	1950 in a limited edition of 150
Series:	Doughty American Birds

			Price	
Colourways	*Backstamp*	*U.S. $*	*Can. $*	*U.K. £*
Dark grey/yellow/white	Black	1,250.00	1,750.00	900.00

RW3431
MEXICAN FEIJOA AND LADYBIRD
Style One

Modeller:	Dorothy Doughty
Height:	10 ¾", 27.8 cm
Colour:	Rose-pink and pale pink flowers; green leaves; grey branch; red ladybird
Plinth:	Wooden
Issued:	1950 in a limited edition of 125

			Price	
Colourways	*Backstamp*	*U.S. $*	*Can. $*	*U.K. £*
Rose-pink/pale pink/green	Black	775.00	1,100.00	550.00

RW3432
MEXICAN FEIJOA AND LADYBIRD
Style Two

Modeller:	Dorothy Doughty
Height:	10 ¾", 27.8 cm
Colour:	Rose-pink and pale pink flowers; green leaves; grey branch; red ladybird
Plinth:	Wooden
Issued:	1950 in a limited edition of 125

			Price	
Colourways	*Backstamp*	*U.S. $*	*Can. $*	*U.K. £*
Rose-pink/pale pink/green	Black	775.00	1,100.00	550.00

RW3434
H.R.H. PRINCESS ELIZABETH ON "TOMMY"

Modeller: Doris Lindner
Height: With plinth: 15", 38.1 cm
Colour: 1. Navy blue uniform; chestnut horse
2. White (Classic)
Plinth: Wooden
Issued: 1948 in a limited edition of 100

Colourways	*Backstamp*	*U.S. $*	*Price Can. $*	*U.K. £*
1. Black/mustard/chestnut	Black	7,000.00	9,000.00	4,000.00
2. White	Black		Very rare	

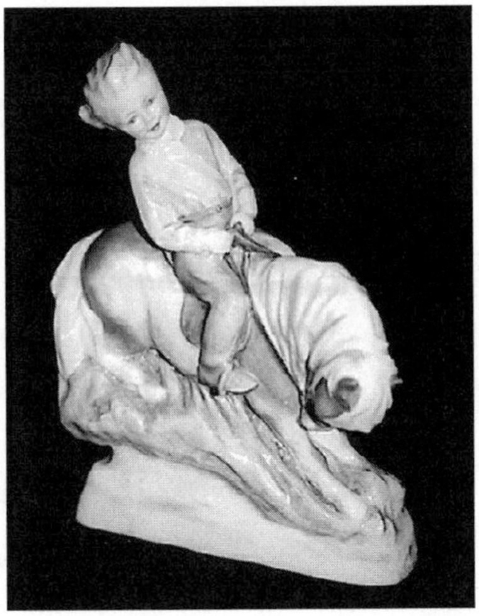

RW3435
HAPPY DAYS

Modeller: Freda Doughty
Height: 7 ½", 19.1 cm
Colour: Light green shirt; blue-grey trousers; yellow hair; cream and brown pony; cream base
Issued: 1948-by 1955

Colourways	*Backstamp*	*U.S. $*	*Price Can. $*	*U.K. £*
Light green/blue-grey	Black	1,900.00	2,500.00	1,100.00

RW3438
RUBY-THROATED HUMMINGBIRD AND FUCHSIA (Cock)
(Archilochus Colubris)

Modeller: Dorothy Doughty
Height: 9 ¼", 23.5 cm
Colour: Green, yellow and grey bird; pink and blue fuchsia; green leaves
Plinth: Wooden
Issued: 1950 in a limited edition of 500
Series: Doughty American Birds

Colourways	*Backstamp*	*U.S. $*	*Price Can. $*	*U.K. £*
Green/yellow/grey/pink/blue	Black	1,250.00	1,750.00	900.00

RW3439
RUBY-THROATED HUMMINGBIRD AND FUCHSIA (Hen)
(Archilochus Colubris)

Modeller: Dorothy Doughty
Height: 9 ¼", 23.5 cm
Colour: Green, yellow and grey bird; brown nest with eggs; pink and blue fuchsia; green leaves
Plinth: Wooden
Issued: 1950 in a limited edition of 500
Series: Doughty American Birds

Colourways	*Backstamp*	*U.S. $*	*Price Can. $*	*U.K. £*
Green/yellow/grey/pink/blue	Black	1,250.00	1,750.00	900.00

RW3462
ALSATIAN
Style Two

Modeller: Doris Lindner
Height: 9 ¾" x 11 ½", 24.7 x 29.2 cm
Colour: 1. Brown with black shading
2. White
Issued: 1950-c.1958
Series: Large Dogs

Colourways	*Backstamp*	*U.S. $*	*Price Can. $*	*U.K. £*
1. Coloured (as above)	Green	800.00	1,000.00	500.00
2. White	Green	600.00	500.00	250.00

RW3463
ENGLISH SETTER / IRISH SETTER

Modeller: Doris Lindner
Height: 8", 20.3 cm
Size: Large
Colour: 1. English Setter: White with black markings
2. Irish Setter: Reddish-brown
Issued: 1950
Series: Large Dogs

Description	*Backstamp*	*U.S. $*	*Price Can. $*	*U.K. £*
1. English Setter	Black	1,200.00	1,200.00	500.00
2. Irish Setter	Black	1,200.00	1,200.00	500.00

Note: Model RW3463 could be painted as either an English or Irish Setter.

RW3464
YELLOW-HEADED BLACKBIRD AND SPIDERWORT (Cock)
(Xanthocephalus Xanthocephalus)

Modeller: Dorothy Doughty
Height: 11", 27.9 cm
Colour: Yellow and black bird; purple-blue flowers; green foliage; green-brown base
Plinth: Wooden
Issued: 1952 in a limited edition of 350
Series: Doughty American Birds

Colourways	Backstamp	Price U.S. $	Can. $	U.K. £
Yellow/black/purple-blue	Black	1,350.00	1,750.00	950.00

RW3465
YELLOW-HEADED BLACKBIRD AND SPIDERWORT (Hen)
(Xanthocephalus Xanthocephalus)

Modeller: Dorothy Doughty
Height: 11", 27.9 cm
Colour: Purple, brown and yellow bird; deep blue flowers; green foliage; green-brown base
Plinth: Wooden
Issued: 1952 in a limited edition of 350
Series: Doughty American Birds

Colourways	Backstamp	Price U.S. $	Can. $	U.K. £
Purple/brown/yellow/blue	Black	1,350.00	1,750.00	950.00

RW3466
WILD HORSES

Modeller: Doris Lindner
Height: 16 ¼", 41.2 cm
Colour: 1. Grey
2. White
Plinth: Wooden, large oval
Issued: 1950-c.1970s
Varieties: Also called "Galloping in Winter" RW3958

Colourways	Backstamp	Price U.S. $	Can. $	U.K. £
1. Coloured (as above)	Black	Very few pieces of this		
2. White	Green	early version were produced		

Note: In 1974 the central support was eliminated, and the model was produced in colour as a limited edition of 250 and entitled "Galloping in Winter."

RW3467
GOLDEN-CROWNED KINGLET AND NOBLE PINE (Single)
(Regulus Satrapa)

Modeller: Dorothy Doughty
Height: 7 ¾", 19.7 cm
Colour: Blue-grey, green, brown, yellow and grey bird; green foliage; brown branch
Plinth: Wooden
Issued: 1952 in a limited edition of 500
Series: Doughty American Birds

Colourways	*Backstamp*	*U.S. $*	*Price Can. $*	*U.K. £*
Blue-grey/green	Black	900.00	1,250.00	650.00

RW3468
GOLDEN CROWNED KINGLET AND NOBLE PINE (Double)
(Regulus Satrapa)

Modeller: Dorothy Doughty
Height: 7 ¾", 19.7 cm
Colour: Green, blue-grey, brown, yellow and grey birds; green foliage; brown branch
Plinth: Wooden
Issued: 1952 in a limited edition of 500
Series: Doughty American Birds

Colourways	*Backstamp*	*U.S. $*	*Price Can. $*	*U.K. £*
Green/blue-grey	Black	1,200.00	1,750.00	850.00

RW3469
RED-EYED VIREO AND SWAMP AZALEA (Cock)
(Vireo Olivaceus)

Modeller: Dorothy Doughty
Height: 7 ¾", 19.7 cm
Colour: Blue-grey, green and grey bird; pink and white blossom; grey-green branch
Plinth: Wooden
Issued: 1952 in a limited edition of 500
Series: Doughty American Birds

Colourways	*Backstamp*	*U.S. $*	*Price Can. $*	*U.K. £*
Blue-grey/green/grey	Black	1,000.00	1,500.00	750.00

RW3470
RED-EYED VIREO AND SWAMP AZALEA (Hen)
(Vireo Olivaceus)

Modeller: Dorothy Doughty
Height: 7 ¾", 19.7 cm
Colour: Blue-grey, green and grey bird; pink and white blossom; grey-green branch
Plinth: Wooden
Issued: 1952 in a limited edition of 500
Series: Doughty American Birds

			Price	
Colourways	*Backstamp*	*U.S. $*	*Can. $*	*U.K. £*
Blue-grey/green/grey	Black	1,000.00	1,500.00	750.00

RW3476
CHAFFINCH (Hen)

Modeller: Dorothy Doughty
Height: Unknown
Colour: Grey and reddish-brown; white flowers; wooden base
Plinth: Wooden
Issued: 1951

			Price	
Colourways	*Backstamp*	*U.S. $*	*Can. $*	*U.K. £*
Grey/reddish-brown	Black	Not put into full production, only a few samples known		

RW3503
THE QUEEN'S BEASTS

Two models make up this style number, one of a dog holding a shield emblazoned with the Tudor rose, the other a horse with a shield with quartered royal arms, both on circular bases. Eleven pairs of these animals were intended to be mounted onto the Queen's Coronation Vase, but a few extra models were produced. They were painted by Harry Davis.

Modeller: Frederick M. Gertner
Height: 5 ½", 14.0 cm
Colour: 1. Dog: White
2. Horse: White horse holds Royal Standard
Issued: 1953

			Price	
Description	*Backstamp*	*U.S. $*	*Can. $*	*U.K. £*
1. Dog	Black	200.00	300.00	150.00
2. Horse	Black	200.00	300.00	150.00

RW3506
BLUE-GREY GNATCATCHER AND DOGWOOD (Single)
(Polioptila Caerulea)

Modeller:	Dorothy Doughty
Height:	11 ½", 29.2 cm
Colour:	Blue-grey and white bird; white flowers; green leaves
Plinth:	Wooden
Issued:	1955 in a limited edition of 500
Series:	Doughty American Birds

Colourways	*Backstamp*	*U.S. $*	*Price Can. $*	*U.K. £*
Blue-grey/white/green	Black	1,350.00	2,000.00	950.00

RW3507
BLUE-GREY GNATCATCHER AND DOGWOOD (Double)
(Polioptila Caerulea)

Modeller:	Dorothy Doughty
Height:	11 ½", 29.2 cm
Colour:	Blue-grey and white birds; white flowers; green leaves
Plinth:	Wooden
Issued:	1955 in a limited edition of 500
Series:	Doughty American Birds

Colourways	*Backstamp*	*U.S. $*	*Price Can. $*	*U.K. £*
Blue-grey/white/green	Black	1,350.00	2,000.00	950.00

RW3508
MYRTLE WARBLER AND WEEPING CHERRY (Cock)
(Dendroica Coronata)

Modeller:	Dorothy Doughty
Height:	9 ½", 24.0 cm
Colour:	Blue, grey, orange amd black bird; pink and white blossom; grey-green branch
Plinth:	Wooden
Issued:	1955 in a limited edition of 500
Series:	Doughty American Birds

Colourways	*Backstamp*	*U.S. $*	*Price Can. $*	*U.K. £*
Blue/grey/orange/black	Black	1,000.00	1,500.00	700.00

RW3509
MYRTLE WARBLER AND WEEPING CHERRY (Hen)
(Dendroica Coronata)

Modeller: Dorothy Doughty
Height: 9 ½", 24.0 cm
Colour: Grey, yellow and black bird; pink and white blossom; grey-green branch
Plinth: Wooden
Issued: 1955 in a limited edition of 500
Series: Doughty American Birds

Colourways	*Backstamp*	*U.S. $*	*Price* *Can. $*	*U.K. £*
Grey-yellow/black	Black	1,000.00	1,500.00	700.00

RW3511
WOLF

Modeller: Miss M. J. Stevens
Height: 8", 20.3 cm
Colour: Brown wolf; greenish-yellow dress; mauve shawl; white base
Issued: 1954

Colourways	*Backstamp*	*U.S. $*	*Price* *Can. $*	*U.K. £*
Brown/green-yellow/mauve	Black		Extremely rare	

RW3512
BEWICK'S WREN AND YELLOW JASMINE (Cock)
(Thryomanes Bewickii)

Modeller: Dorothy Doughty
Height: 10", 25.4 cm
Colour: Brown with cream breast; yellow flowers; green leaves; green-brown branch
Plinth: Wooden
Issued: 1956 in a limited edition of 500
Series: Doughty American Birds

Colourways	*Backstamp*	*U.S. $*	*Price* *Can. $*	*U.K. £*
Brown/cream/yellow/green	Black	1,250.00	1,750.00	850.00

RW3513
BEWICK'S WREN AND YELLOW JASMINE (Hen)
(Thryomanes Bewickii)

Modeller:	Dorothy Doughty
Height:	10", 25.4 cm
Colour:	Brown with cream breast; yellow flowers; green leaves; green-brown branch
Plinth:	Wooden
Issued:	1956 in a limited edition of 500
Series:	Doughty American Birds

Colourways	*Backstamp*	*U.S. $*	*Price Can. $*	*U.K. £*
Brown/cream/yellow/green	Black	1,250.00	1,750.00	850.00

RW3514
FOALS (Without base)

Modeller:	Doris Lindner
Height:	5", 12.7 cm
Colour:	Light tan; dark tan; light green base
Issued:	1954
Varieties:	Foals (With base) RW3152

Colourways	*Backstamp*	*U.S. $*	*Price Can. $*	*U.K. £*
Light tan/dark tan	Black	600.00	850.00	425.00

RW3515
CALVES (Without base)

Modeller:	Doris Lindner
Height:	3 ½", 8.9 cm
Colour:	White and red-brown
Issued:	1954
Varieties:	Calves (With base) RW3146

Colourways	*Backstamp*	*U.S. $*	*Price Can. $*	*U.K. £*
White/red-brown	Black	525.00	750.00	375.00

RW3516
MAYTIME (Without base)

Modeller: Doris Lindner
Height: 3", 7.6 cm
Colour: Creamy white
Issued: 1954
Varieties: Maytime (With base) RW3123

Colourways	Backstamp	Price U.S. $	Price Can. $	Price U.K. £
Creamy white	Black	450.00	650.00	325.00

RW3517
KIDS AT PLAY (Without base)

Modeller: Doris Lindner
Height: 4 ¼", 10.8 cm
Colour: Grey-blue and white
Issued: 1954
Varieties: Kids at Play (With base) RW3153
Series: Goats

Colourways	Backstamp	Price U.S. $	Price Can. $	Price U.K. £
Grey-blue/white	Black	450.00	650.00	325.00

RW3525
SCARLET TANAGER AND WHITE OAK (Cock)
(Piranga Olivacea)

Modeller: Dorothy Doughty
Height: 11", 27.9 cm
Colour: Scarlet and black bird; green foliage; brown branch
Plinth: Wooden
Issued: 1956 in a limited edition of 500
Series: Doughty American Birds

Colourways	Backstamp	Price U.S. $	Price Can. $	Price U.K. £
Scarlet/black/green/brown	Black	1,350.00	1,950.00	950.00

RW3526
SCARLET TANAGER AND WHITE OAK (Hen)
(Piranga Olivacea)

Modeller: Dorothy Doughty
Height: 11", 27.9 cm
Colour: Yellow bird, orange beak;
green foliage; brown-grey branch
Plinth: Wooden
Issued: 1956 in a limited edition of 500
Series: Doughty American Birds

Colourways	*Backstamp*	*U.S. $*	*Price Can. $*	*U.K. £*
Yellow/orange/green	Black	1,350.00	1,950.00	950.00

RW3527
FOX (Lying, without base)

Modeller: Doris Lindner
Length: 4", 10.1 cm
Colour: Chestnut red fox
Issued: 1954
Varieties: Fox (Lying, on curved base) RW2950;
Fox Ashtray RW2873;
Fox Tobacco Jar RW2925

Colourways	*Backstamp*	*U.S. $*	*Price Can. $*	*U.K. £*
Chestnut red	Black	250.00	350.00	175.00

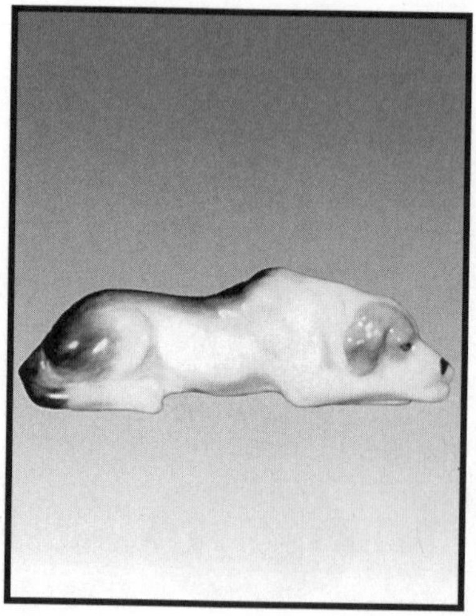

RW3528
HOUND (Lying straight, without base)
Style One

Modeller: Doris Lindner
Length: 4", 10.1 cm
Colour: White with chestnut brown and black spots
Issued: 1954
Varieties: Hound (Lying, on straight base) RW2926

Colourways	*Backstamp*	*U.S. $*	*Price Can. $*	*U.K. £*
White/brown/black	Black	250.00	350.00	175.00

RW3529
FAWNS, YOUNG SPOTTED DEER (Without base)

Modeller: Doris Lindner
Height: 3 ½", 8.9 cm
Colour: Brown with white markings
Issued: 1952
Varieties: Fawns, Young Spotted Deer (Rectangular base) RW3266;
Fawns, Young Spotted Deer (Oval base) RW3316
Series: Zoo Babies

			Price	
Colourways	*Backstamp*	*U.S. $*	*Can. $*	*U.K. £*
Brown	Black	775.00	1,100.00	550.00

RW3530
GOAT (Head raised, without base)

Modeller: Henri Bargas
Height: 5", 12.7 cm
Colour: White with black markings
Issued: 1954
Varieties: Goat (Head raised, with base) RW3125
Series: Goats

			Price	
Colourways	*Backstamp*	*U.S. $*	*Can. $*	*U.K. £*
White/black/green	Black	600.00	850.00	425.00

RW3531
GOAT (Licking hind leg, without base)

Modeller: Henri Bargas
Height: 4 ½", 11.9 cm
Colour: White with black markings
Issued: 1954
Varieties: Goat (Licking hind leg, with base) RW3124
Series: Goats

			Price	
Colourways	*Backstamp*	*U.S. $*	*Can. $*	*U.K. £*
White/black/green	Black	525.00	750.00	375.00

RW3532
OVENBIRD WITH LADY'S SLIPPER (Cock)
(Seiurus Aurocapillus)

Modeller:	Dorothy Doughty
Height:	11", 27.9 cm
Colour:	Green-brown, blue, grey and black bird; blue lady's slipper flowers; green and brown leaves
Plinth:	Wooden
Issued:	1957 in a limited edition of 250
Series:	Doughty American Birds

			Price	
Colourways	*Backstamp*	*U.S. $*	*Can. $*	*U.K. £*
Green-brown/blue/grey/black	Black	1,250.00	1,750.00	900.00

RW3533
OVENBIRD WITH CRESTED IRIS (Hen)
(Seiurus Aurocapillus)

Modeller:	Dorothy Doughty
Height:	11", 27.9 cm
Colour:	Green-brown, blue, grey and black bird; mauve iris; green and brown leaves
Plinth:	Wooden
Issued:	1957 in a limited edition of 250
Series:	Doughty American Birds

			Price	
Colourways	*Backstamp*	*U.S. $*	*Can. $*	*U.K. £*
Green-brown/blue/grey/black	Black	1,250.00	1,750.00	900.00

RW3536
PARULA WARBLER AND SWEET BAY (Cock)
(Parula Americana)

Modeller:	Dorothy Doughty
Height:	9", 22.9 cm
Colour:	Grey-green, yellow and white bird; white flower and bud; green leaves; grey-brown branch
Plinth:	Wooden
Issued:	1957 in a limited edition of 500
Series:	Doughty American Birds

			Price	
Colourways	*Backstamp*	*U.S. $*	*Can. $*	*U.K. £*
Grey-green/yellow/white	Black	1,350.00	1,950.00	950.00

RW3537
PARULA WARBLER AND SWEET BAY (Hen)
(Parula Americana)

Modeller: Dorothy Doughty
Height: 9", 22.9 cm
Colour: Blue, yellow and white bird; white flower and bud; green leaves; green-brown branch
Plinth: Wooden
Issued: 1957 in a limited edition of 500
Series: Doughty American Birds

			Price	
Colourways	*Backstamp*	*U.S. $*	*Can. $*	*U.K. £*
Blue/yellow/white/green	Black	1,350.00	1,950.00	950.00

RW3539
YELLOW-THROAT AND WATER HYACINTH (Cock)
(Geothlypis Trichas)

Modeller: Dorothy Doughty
Height: 11", 27.9 cm
Colour: Greenish-purple and yellow bird; lilac, blue and yellow flowers; greenish-yellow leaves
Plinth: Wooden
Issued: 1958 in a limited edition of 350
Series: Doughty American Birds

			Price	
Colourways	*Backstamp*	*U.S. $*	*Can. $*	*U.K. £*
Greenish-purple/yellow	Black	1,750.00	2,500.00	1,200.00

RW3540
YELLOW-THROAT AND WATER HYACINTH (Hen)
(Geothlypis Trichas)

Modeller: Dorothy Doughty
Height: 11", 27.9 cm
Colour: Greenish-purple, yellow and black bird; lilac, yellow and blue flowers; greenish-white leaves
Plinth: Wooden
Issued: 1958 in a limited edition of 350
Series: Doughty American Birds

			Price	
Colourways	*Backstamp*	*U.S. $*	*Can. $*	*U.K. £*
Greenish-purple/yellow/black	Black	1,750.00	2,500.00	1,200.00

RW3548
PHOEBE AND FLAME VINE (Cock)
(Sayornis Phoebe)

Modeller:	Dorothy Doughty
Height:	9 ¾", 24.7 cm
Colour:	Blue-grey, green and yellowish-grey bird; orange flowers; green leaves; green-brown branch
Plinth:	Wooden
Issued:	1958 in a limited edition of 500
Series:	Doughty American Birds

Colourways	*Backstamp*	*U.S. $*	*Price Can. $*	*U.K. £*
Blue-grey/green/yellow/orange	Black	1,500.00	2,000.00	1,000.00

RW3549
PHOEBE AND FLAME VINE (Hen)
(Sayornis Phoebe)

Modeller:	Dorothy Doughty
Height:	9 ¾", 24.7 cm
Colour:	Brown and grey bird; orange flowers; green leaves; grey-green branch
Plinth:	Wooden
Issued:	1958 in a limited edition of 500
Series:	Doughty American Birds

Colourways	*Backstamp*	*U.S. $*	*Price Can. $*	*U.K. £*
Brown/grey/orange/green	Black	1,500.00	2,000.00	1,000.00

RW3561
CHANTICLEER (Cockerel)

Modeller:	Doris Lindner
Height:	11", 27.9 cm
Colour:	1. Unglazed biscuit 2. White with green and mauve highlights; red comb; yellow beak
Issued:	1955

Colourways	*Backstamp*	*U.S. $*	*Price Can. $*	*U.K. £*
1. Biscuit	Black	225.00	300.00	150.00
2. White/green/mauve	Black	500.00	700.00	350.00

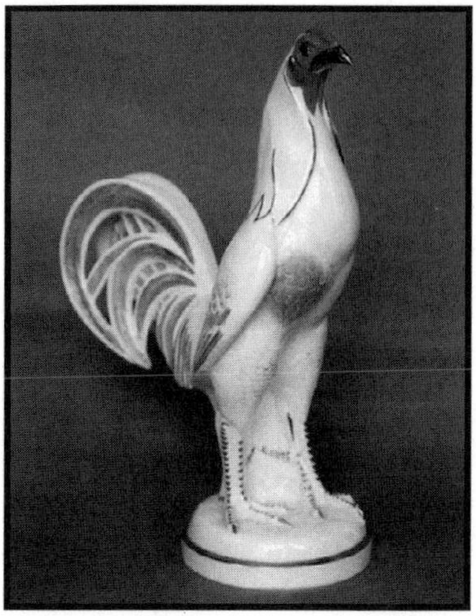

RW3562
GAMECOCK

Modeller: Doris Lindner
Height: 13", 33.0 cm
Colour: 1. Unglazed biscuit
2. White with green and gold highlights; red head
Issued: 1955

			Price	
Colourways	*Backstamp*	*U.S. $*	*Can. $*	*U.K. £*
1. Biscuit	Black	225.00	300.00	150.00
2. White/green/gold	Black	500.00	700.00	350.00

See page 32
for this model
with a base

RW3570
FOX (Lying straight, without base)

Modeller: Doris Lindner
Height: 4 ½", 11.9 cm
Colour: Reddish-brown
Issued: 1956
Varieties: Fox (Lying, on straight base) RW2997

			Price	
Colourways	*Backstamp*	*U.S. $*	*Can. $*	*U.K. £*
Reddish-brown	Black	300.00	450.00	225.00

RW3571
HOUND (Lying straight, without base)
Style Two

Modeller: Doris Lindner
Size: 1 ¼" x 5", 3.2 x 12.7 cm
Colour: White with dark brown and black patches
Issued: 1956
Varieties: Hound (Lying, on straight base) RW2998

			Price	
Colourways	*Backstamp*	*U.S. $*	*Can. $*	*U.K. £*
White/brown/black	Black	300.00	450.00	225.00

RW3572
RED HIND FISH
Style One

Modeller: Ronald Van Ruyckevelt
Height: 5 ½", 14.0 cm
Colour: 1. Cream with red spots; black-edged fins; orange mouth; mauve rocks
2. White
Issued: 1956-c.1975
Series: Tropical Fish (Small size)

Colourways	*Backstamp*	*U.S. $*	*Price Can. $*	*U.K. £*
1. Coloured (as above)	Black	225.00	325.00	160.00
2. White	Green	150.00	200.00	100.00

RW3573
FOUR-EYED BUTTERFLY FISH

Modeller: Ronald Van Ruyckevelt
Height: 5 ½", 14.0 cm
Colour: 1. Pink-brown with yellow and black stripes
2. White
Issued: 1956-c.1975
Series: Tropical Fish (Small size)

Colourways	*Backstamp*	*U.S. $*	*Price Can. $*	*U.K. £*
1. Coloured (as above)	Black	225.00	325.00	160.00
2. White	Green	150.00	200.00	100.00

RW3574
BLUE ANGEL FISH
Style One

Modeller: Ronald Van Ruyckevelt
Height: 5 ½", 14.0 cm
Colour: 1. Pink, blue and yellow fish; pink and brown coral
2. White
Issued: 1956-c.1975
Series: Tropical Fish (Small size)

Colourways	*Backstamp*	*U.S. $*	*Price Can. $*	*U.K. £*
1. Coloured (as above)	Black	225.00	325.00	160.00
2. White	Green	150.00	200.00	100.00

RW3575
SERGEANT-MAJOR FISH

Modeller: Ronald Van Ruyckevelt
Height: 5 ½″, 14.0 cm
Colour: 1. Bluish-green; yellow shading; black stripes
2. White
Issued: 1956-c.1975
Series: Tropical Fish (Small size)

Colourways	*Backstamp*	*U.S. $*	*Price Can. $*	*U.K. £*
1. Coloured (as above)	Black	225.00	325.00	160.00
2. White	Green	150.00	200.00	100.00

RW3576
YELLOW GRUNT FISH

Modeller: Ronald Van Ruyckevelt
Height: 5 ½″, 14.0 cm
Colour: 1. Yellow-orange with dark blue stripes; green-mauve coral
2. White
Issued: 1956-c.1975
Series: Tropical Fish (Small size)

Colourways	*Backstamp*	*U.S. $*	*Price Can. $*	*U.K. £*
1. Coloured (as above)	Black	225.00	325.00	160.00
2. White	Green	100.00	200.00	100.00

RW3577
FOUR-EYED FISH AND BANDED BUTTERFLY

Modeller: Ronald Van Ruyckevelt
Height: 12″, 30.5 cm
Colour: Upper fish: Black and pale blue
Lower fish: Grey, yellow, black and blue
Coral: Pink, yellow and blue
Plinth: Wooden
Issued: 1957 in a limited edition of 500
Series: Tropical Fish (Large size)

Colourways	*Backstamp*	*U.S. $*	*Price Can. $*	*U.K. £*
Black/pale blue/grey/yellow	Black	650.00	900.00	450.00

RW3578
SPANISH HOG AND SERGEANT-MAJOR FISH

Modeller:	Ronald Van Ruyckevelt
Height:	12", 30.5 cm
Colour:	Upper fish: Purple, blue and yellow Lower fish: Blue, yellow and black Coral: Purple, green, blue and yellow
Plinth:	Wooden
Issued:	1956 in a limited edition of 500
Series:	Tropical Fish (Large size)

			Price	
Colourways	*Backstamp*	*U.S. $*	*Can. $*	*U.K. £*
Purple/blue/yellow/black	Black	650.00	900.00	450.00

RW3579
SPADE FISH

Modeller:	Ronald Van Ruyckevelt
Height:	5 ½", 14.0 cm
Colour:	1. Pearly grey and black stripes; green and pink coral 2. White
Issued:	1956-c.1975
Series:	Tropical Fish (Small size)

			Price	
Colourways	*Backstamp*	*U.S. $*	*Can. $*	*U.K. £*
1. Coloured (as above)	Black	225.00	325.00	160.00
2. White	Green	150.00	200.00	100.00

RW3581
LISERION (Bird)

Modeller:	A. Azori
Height:	9", 22.9 cm
Colour:	1. Naturalistically coloured 2. White biscuit porcelain
Issued:	1956

			Price	
Colourways	*Backstamp*	*U.S. $*	*Can. $*	*U.K. £*
1. Natural	Black	500.00	700.00	350.00
2. White	Green	225.00	300.00	150.00

RW3582
MARGUERITE (Cockerel)

Modeller: A. Azori
Height: 9", 22.9 cm
Colour: 1. Naturalistically coloured
2. White biscuit porcelain
Issued: 1956

Colourways	Backstamp	U.S. $	Price Can. $	U.K. £
1. Natural	Black	500.00	700.00	350.00
2. White	Green	225.00	300.00	150.00

RW3583
COQUELICOT (Bird)

Modeller: A. Azori
Height: 9", 22.9 cm
Colour: 1. Naturalistically coloured
2. White biscuit porcelain
Issued: 1956

Colourways	Backstamp	U.S. $	Price Can. $	U.K. £
1. Natural	Black	500.00	700.00	350.00
2. White	Green	225.00	300.00	150.00

RW3584
ANEMONE (Bird)

Modeller: A. Azori
Height: 9", 22.9 cm
Colour: 1. Naturalistically coloured
2. White biscuit porcelain
Issued: 1956

Colourways	Backstamp	U.S. $	Price Can. $	U.K. £
1. Natural	Black	500.00	700.00	350.00
2. White	Green	225.00	300.00	150.00

RW3590
HOODED WARBLER AND CHEROKEE ROSE (Cock)
(Wilsonia Critina)

Modeller:	Dorothy Doughty
Height:	10 ½", 26.0 cm
Colour:	Yellow, green and black bird; white flower and bud; green foliage; grey-green base
Plinth:	Wooden
Issued:	1961 in a limited edition of 500
Series:	Doughty American Birds

			Price	
Colourways	*Backstamp*	*U.S. $*	*Can. $*	*U.K. £*
Yellow/green/black/white	Black	775.00	1,100.00	550.00

RW3591
HOODED WARBLER AND CHEROKEE ROSE (Hen)
(Wilsonia Critina)

Modeller:	Dorothy Doughty
Height:	10 ½", 26.0 cm
Colour:	Yellow and mauve bird; white flowers and bud; green foliage; green-brown base
Plinth:	Wooden
Issued:	1961 in a limited edition of 500
Series:	Doughty American Birds

			Price	
Colourways	*Backstamp*	*U.S. $*	*Can. $*	*U.K. £*
Yellow/mauve/white/green	Black	775.00	1,100.00	550.00

RW3592
DOWNY WOODPECKER AND PECAN (Cock)
(Dendrocopus Pubescens)

Modeller:	Dorothy Doughty
Height:	10", 25.4 cm
Colour:	1. Dark grey, white and red bird; green leaves; brown-green branch 2. White
Plinth:	Wooden
Issued:	1. Coloured: 1967 in a limited edition of 500 2. White: 1967 in a limited edition of 75
Series:	Doughty American Birds

			Price	
Colourways	*Backstamp*	*U.S. $*	*Can. $*	*U.K. £*
1. Coloured (as above)	Black	1,250.00	1,750.00	850.00
2. White	Black	300.00	400.00	200.00

RW3593
DOWNY WOODPECKER AND PECAN (Hen)
(Dendrocopus Pubescens)

Modeller: Dorothy Doughty
Height: 10", 25.4 cm
Colour: 1. Brown, dark grey and white bird; green leaves; brown-grey branch
2. White
Plinth: Wooden
Issued: 1. Coloured: 1967 in a limited edition of 500
2. White: 1967 in a limited edition of 75
Series: Doughty American Birds

Colourways	*Backstamp*	*U.S. $*	*Price Can. $*	*U.K. £*
1. Coloured (as above)	Black	500.00	700.00	350.00
2. White	Black	300.00	400.00	200.00

RW3602
RED HIND FISH
Style Two

Modeller: Ronald Van Ruyckevelt
Height: 12 ¾", 32.4 cm
Colour: White with pink dots and stripes; yellow and black fins
Plinth: Wooden
Issued: 1956 in a limited edition of 500
Series: Tropical Fish (Large size)

Colourways	*Backstamp*	*U.S. $*	*Price Can. $*	*U.K. £*
White/pink	Black	650.00	900.00	450.00

RW3603
BLUE ANGEL FISH
Style Two

Modeller: Ronald Van Ruyckevelt
Height: 12", 30.5 cm
Colour: Blue, green and yellow
Plinth: Wooden
Issued: 1956 in a limited edition of 500
Series: Tropical Fish (Large size)

Colourways	*Backstamp*	*U.S. $*	*Price Can. $*	*U.K. £*
Blue/green/yellow	Black	650.00	900.00	450.00

RW3604
SQUIRREL FISH

Modeller:	Ronald Van Ruyckevelt
Height:	10 ½", 26.7 cm
Colour:	Pink fish
Plinth:	Wooden
Issued:	1956 in a limited edition of 500
Series:	Tropical Fish (Large size)

Colourways	*Backstamp*	*U.S. $*	*Price Can. $*	*U.K. £*
Pink	Black	650.00	900.00	450.00

RW3605
ROCK BEAUTY FISH

Modeller:	Ronald Van Ruyckevelt
Height:	10", 30.5 cm
Colour:	Black, green and yellow
Plinth:	Wooden
Issued:	1956 in a limited edition of 500
Series:	Tropical Fish (Large size)

Colourways	*Backstamp*	*U.S. $*	*Price Can. $*	*U.K. £*
Black/green/yellow	Black	650.00	900.00	450.00

RW3606
RAINBOW PARROT FISH

Modeller:	Ronald Van Ruyckevelt
Height:	12", 30.5 cm
Colour:	Unknown
Plinth:	Wooden
Issued:	1956 in a limited edition of 500
Series:	Tropical Fish (Large size)

Colourways	*Backstamp*	*U.S. $*	*Price Can. $*	*U.K. £*
Unknown	Black	650.00	900.00	450.00

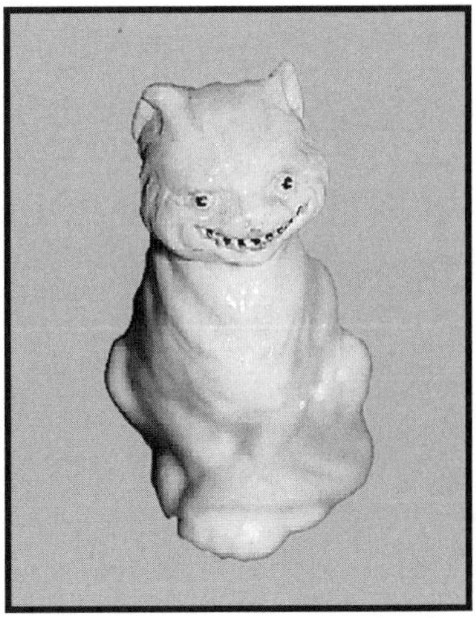

RW3609
CHESHIRE CAT

Modeller: Freda Doughty
Height: 3 ½", 8.9 cm
Colour: Grey with white markings
Issued: 1957-1959
Series: Alice in Wonderland

Colourways	*Backstamp*	*U.S. $*	*Price* *Can. $*	*U.K. £*
Grey	Black	1,000.00	1,350.00	600.00

RW3610
MOCK TURTLE

Modeller: Freda Doughty
Height: 3 ¼", 8.3 cm
Colour: Brown head; green flippers; yellow shell
Issued: 1957-1959
Series: Alice in Wonderland

Colourways	*Backstamp*	*U.S. $*	*Price* *Can. $*	*U.K. £*
Brown/green/yellow	Black	875.00	1,125.00	500.00

Note: The Mock Turtle is a hollow-based figure and not a candle-snuffer.

RW3611
WHITE RABBIT

Modeller: Freda Doughty
Height: 4", 10.1 cm
Colour: Red coat; yellow waistcoat; black buttons and bow-tie; white gloves
Issued: 1957-1959
Series: Alice in Wonderland

Colourways	*Backstamp*	*U.S. $*	*Price* *Can. $*	*U.K. £*
Red/yellow/black/white	Black	1,125.00	1,450.00	650.00

RW3613
THE DODO

Modeller: Freda Doughty
Height: 3 ¼", 8.3 cm
Colour: 1. Brown back; yellow breast; cream and yellow face; red eyes, beak and feet; brown cane
2. Pale brown back; yellow breast; pale green and yellow face; blue cuffs; pink eyes, beak and feet; pale brown cane
Issued: 1957-1959
Series: Alice in Wonderland

			Price	
Colourways	*Backstamp*	*U.S. $*	*Can. $*	*U.K. £*
Coloured (as above)	Black	850.00	1,100.00	480.00

RW3615
LONG-HAIRED CAT

Modeller: Freda Doughty
Height: 4", 10.1 cm
Colour: 1. Ginger and white
2. Grey and white
Issued: 1957

			Price	
Colourways	*Backstamp*	*U.S. $*	*Can. $*	*U.K. £*
Coloured (as above)	Black	200.00	300.00	150.00

RW3616
SHORT-HAIRED CAT

Modeller: Freda Doughty
Height: 3", 7.5 cm
Colour: White with brown markings
Issued: 1957

			Price	
Colourways	*Backstamp*	*U.S. $*	*Can. $*	*U.K. £*
White/brown	Black	175.00	250.00	125.00

RW3617
ELF OWL AND SAGUARO
(Micropallas Whitneyi Whitneyi)

Modeller: Dorothy Doughty
Height: 11", 27.9 cm
Colour: Grey and white bird; white flowers with yellow centres; green foliage base
Plinth: Wooden
Issued: 1958 in a limited edition of 500
Series: Doughty American Birds

Colourways	*Backstamp*	*U.S. $*	*Price* *Can. $*	*U.K. £*
Grey/white/yellow/green	Black	1,350.00	1,950.00	950.00

RW3618
CACTUS WREN AND PRICKLY PEAR (Cock)
(Heleodytis Brunneicapillus Couesi)

Modeller: Dorothy Doughty
Height: 10 ½", 26.7 cm
Colour: Black, yellow and white bird; yellow flowers; mauve and green cactus; red, yellow and black snake; green-brown base
Plinth: Wooden
Issued: 1959 in a limited edition of 500
Series: Doughty American Birds

Colourways	*Backstamp*	*U.S. $*	*Price* *Can. $*	*U.K. £*
Black/yellow/white/yellow	Black	1,250.00	1,750.00	900.00

RW3619
CACTUS WREN AND PRICKLY PEAR (Hen)
(Heleodytis Brunneicapillus Couesi)

Modeller: Dorothy Doughty
Height: 10 ½", 26.7 cm
Colour: Browns, black and white bird; yellow flowers; mauve and green cactus; brown base
Plinth: Wooden
Issued: 1959 in a limited edition of 500
Series: Doughty American Birds

Colourways	*Backstamp*	*U.S. $*	*Price* *Can. $*	*U.K. £*
Browns/black/white/yellow	Black	1,250.00	1,750.00	900.00

RW3622
OFFICER OF THE LIFE GUARDS

Modeller: Doris Lindner
Heights: 9″, 22.9 cm
Colour: Red, white and black
Plinth: Wooden
Issued: 1957 in a limited edition of 150

Colourways	Backstamp	U.S. $	Price Can. $	U.K. £
Red/white/black	Black	1,500.00	1,850.00	900.00

RW3623
OFFICE OF THE BLUES

Modeller: Doris Lindner
Heights: 9″, 22.9 cm
Colour: Blue, white and black
Plinth: Wooden
Issued: 1957 in a limited edition of 150

Colourways	Backstamp	U.S. $	Price Can. $	U.K. £
Red/white/black	Black	1,500.00	1,850.00	900.00

RW3627
SCISSOR-TAILED FLYCATCHERS (Wall hanging)
(Muscivora Forficata)

Modeller: Dorothy Doughty
Length: 24″, 61.0 cm
Colour: 1. Blue, green-brown and orange
2. White
Issued: 1. Coloured: 1957 in a limited edition of 250
2. White: 1957 in a limited edition of 75
Series: Doughty American Birds

Colourways	Backstamp	U.S. $	Price Can. $	U.K. £
1. Coloured (as above)	Black	850.00	1,250.00	600.00
2. White	Black	425.00	600.00	300.00

RW3632
EXTINCT CAROLINA PAROQUETS (Wall hanging)
(Conuropsis Carolinensis)

Modeller: Dorothy Doughty
Length: 15", 38.1 cm
Colour: 1. Green, blue, yellow and red
2. White
Issued: 1. Coloured: 1957 in a limited edition of 250
2. White: 1957 in a limited edition of 75
Series: Doughty American Birds

			Price	
Colourways	*Backstamp*	*U.S. $*	*Can. $*	*U.K. £*
1. Coloured (as above)	Black	850.00	1,250.00	600.00
2. White	Black	425.00	600.00	300.00

RW3639
CANYON WREN AND WILD LUPIN (Cock)
(Catherpes Mexicanus)

Modeller: Dorothy Doughty
Height: 8", 20.3 cm
Colour: Brown-green and grey bird; mauve-blue flowers; greeen leaves; brown base
Plinth: Wooden
Issued: 1961 in a limited edition of 500
Series: Doughty American Birds

			Price	
Colourways	*Backstamp*	*U.S. $*	*Can. $*	*U.K. £*
Brown-green/grey/mauve-blue	Black	900.00	1,250.00	650.00

RW3640
CANYON WREN AND WILD LUPIN (Hen)
(Catherpes Mexicanus)

Modeller: Dorothy Doughty
Height: 8", 20.3 cm
Colour: Brown-green, grey and russet bird; mauve-blue flowers; green leaves; brown base
Plinth: Wooden
Issued: 1961 in a limited edition of 500
Series: Doughty American Birds

			Price	
Colourways	*Backstamp*	*U.S. $*	*Can. $*	*U.K. £*
Brown-green/grey/russet	Black	900.00	1,250.00	650.00

RW3645
CARDINAL

Modeller: Ronald Van Ruyckevelt
Height: 3 ¼", 8.3 cm
Colour: Red with black highlights
Issued: 1958-1977
Series: Small American Birds

Colourways	*Backstamp*	*U.S. $*	*Price Can. $*	*U.K. £*
Red	Black	75.00	100.00	50.00

RW3646
BLUE JAY (American Version)

Modeller: Ronald Van Ruyckevelt
Height: 3 ¼", 8.3 cm
Colour: Light brown, light blue and grey
Issued: 1958-1977
Series: Small American Birds

Colourways	*Backstamp*	*U.S. $*	*Price Can. $*	*U.K. £*
Light brown	Black	75.00	100.00	50.00

RW3647
AMERICAN ROBIN

Modeller: Ronald Van Ruyckevelt
Height: 4", 10.1 cm
Colour: Brown with black head and wing feathers; yellow beak
Issued: 1958-1977
Series: Small American Birds

Colourways	*Backstamp*	*U.S. $*	*Price Can. $*	*U.K. £*
Brown	Black	75.00	100.00	50.00

RW3648
WAX WING

Modeller:	Ronald Van Ruyckevelt
Height:	3″, 7.6 cm
Colour:	Orange and black
Issued:	1958-1977
Series:	Small American Birds

			Price	
Colourways	*Backstamp*	*U.S. $*	*Can. $*	*U.K. £*
Orange	Black	75.00	100.00	50.00

RW3649
BLUEBIRD

Modeller:	Ronald Van Ruyckevelt
Height:	3″, 7.6 cm
Colour:	Light blue and orange
Issued:	1958-1977
Series:	Small American Birds

			Price	
Colourways	*Backstamp*	*U.S. $*	*Can. $*	*U.K. £*
Light blue/orange	Black	75.00	100.00	50.00

RW3650
WESTERN TANAGER

Modeller:	Ronald Van Ruyckevelt
Height:	2 ½″, 5.7 cm
Colour:	Yellow; red head, black and yellow wings
Issued:	1958-1977
Series:	Small American Birds

			Price	
Colourways	*Backstamp*	*U.S. $*	*Can. $*	*U.K. £*
Yellow/red/black	Black	75.00	100.00	50.00

RW3651
LAZULI BUNTING AND CHOKE CHERRY (Cock)
(Passerina Amoena)

Modeller: Dorothy Doughty
Height: 10", 25.4 cm
Colour: 1. Blue, white and russet bird; white blossom; green leaves; grey-brown branch
2. White
Plinth: Wooden
Issued: 1. Coloured: 1958 in a limited edition of 500
2. White: 1958 in a limited edition of 250
Series: Doughty American Birds

Colourways	*Backstamp*	*U.S. $*	*Price Can. $*	*U.K. £*
1. Coloured (as above)	Black	1,250.00	1,750.00	850.00
2. White	Black	350.00	500.00	250.00

RW3652
LAZULI BUNTING AND CHOKE CHERRY (Hen)
(Passerina Amoena)

Modeller: Dorothy Doughty
Height: 10", 25.4 cm
Colour: 1. Mauve, blue and brown bird; white blossom; green leaves; grey-brown branch
2. White
Plinth: Wooden
Issued: 1. Coloured: 1958 in a limited edition of 500
2. White: 1958 in a limited edition of 250
Series: Doughty American Birds

Colourways	*Backstamp*	*U.S. $*	*Price Can. $*	*U.K. £*
1. Coloured (as above)	Black	1,250.00	1,750.00	850.00
2. White	Black	350.00	500.00	250.00

RW3657
VERMILION FLYCATCHER AND PUSSY WILLOW (Cock)
(Pyrocephalus Rubinus Mexicanus)

Modeller: Dorothy Doughty
Height: 9 ¼", 23.5 cm
Colour: Red and brown bird; yellow pussy willow; green-brown base and stem
Plinth: Wooden
Issued: 1962 in a limited edition of 500
Series: Doughty American Birds

Colourways	*Backstamp*	*U.S. $*	*Price Can. $*	*U.K. £*
Red/brown/yellow	Black	1,000.00	1,500.00	750.00

RW3658
VERMILION FLYCATCHER AND PUSSY WILLOW (Hen)
(Pyrocephalus Rubinus Mexicanus)

Modeller: Dorothy Doughty
Height: 9 ¼", 23.5 cm
Colour: Green-brown and dull yellow bird; yellow flowers; green-brown base and stem
Plinth: Wooden
Issued: 1962 in a limited edition of 500
Series: Doughty American Birds

Colourways	*Backstamp*	*U.S. $*	*Price* *Can. $*	*U.K. £*
Green-brown/yellow	Black	1,000.00	1,500.00	750.00

RW3659
CERULEAN WARBLER AND RED MAPLE (Cock)
(Dendroica Cerulea)

Modeller: Dorothy Doughty
Height: 8 ½", 21.6 cm
Colour: Blue, black and white bird; green and red foliage; green-grey base
Plinth: Wooden
Issued: 1965 in a limited edition of 500
Series: Doughty American Birds

Colourways	*Backstamp*	*U.S. $*	*Price* *Can. $*	*U.K. £*
Blue/black/white	Black	1,000.00	1,500.00	750.00

RW3660
CERULEAN WARBLER AND RED MAPLE (Hen)
(Dendroica Cerulea)

Modeller: Dorothy Doughty
Height: 8 ½", 21.6 cm
Colour: Blue-grey and creamy yellow bird; green and red foliage; green-grey base
Plinth: Wooden
Issued: 1965 in a limited edition of 500
Series: Doughty American Birds

Colourways	*Backstamp*	*U.S. $*	*Price* *Can. $*	*U.K. £*
Blue-grey/creamy yellow	Black	1,000.00	1,500.00	750.00

RW3665
MOUNTAIN BLUEBIRD AND SPLEENWORT NIGER (Cock)
(Sialia Currucoides)

Modeller:	Dorothy Doughty
Height:	9 ½", 24.1 cm
Colour:	Blue and white bird; green foliage; green-grey base
Plinth:	Wooden
Issued:	1964 in a limited edition of 500
Series:	Doughty American Birds

Colourways	*Backstamp*	*U.S. $*	*Price Can. $*	*U.K. £*
Blue/white/green	Black	750.00	1,000.00	500.00

RW3666
MOUNTAIN BLUEBIRD AND SPLEENWORT NIGER (Hen)
(Sialia Currucoides)

Modeller:	Dorothy Doughty
Height:	9 ½", 24.1 cm
Colour:	Blue and white bird; green foliage; green-grey base
Plinth:	Wooden
Issued:	1964 in a limited edition of 500
Series:	Doughty American Birds

Colourways	*Backstamp*	*U.S. $*	*Price Can. $*	*U.K. £*
Blue/white/green	Black	750.00	1,000.00	500.00

RW3667
THE WINNER WITH JOCKEY AND STABLE BOY

Modeller:	Doris Lindner
Height:	11 ¼", 28.5 cm
Colour:	1. Grey 2. Brown
Issued:	1959-1959

Colourways	*Backstamp*	*U.S. $*	*Price Can. $*	*U.K. £*
Coloured (as above)	Black		Extremely rare	

Note: To make production more practical, the stable boy was eliminated from model RW3667 and the plinth was shortened slightly. Although the jockey came painted in the Queen's racing colours, for an extra fee, the colours could be customized.

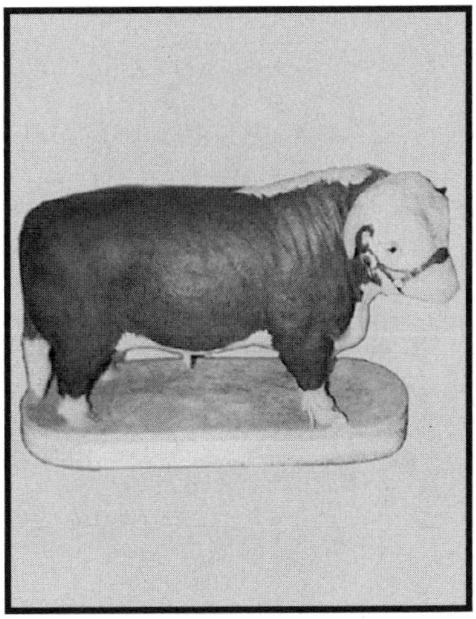

RW3668
HEREFORD BULL "VERN INSPIRATION"

Modeller: Doris Lindner
Height: 7", 17.8 cm
Colour: Reddish-brown and white
Plinth: Wooden
Issued: 1959 in a limited edition of 1,000
Series: Prize Cattle

Colourways	*Backstamp*	*U.S. $*	*Price* *Can. $*	*U.K. £*
Reddish-brown/white	Black	1,000.00	1,250.00	600.00

RW3669
AUDUBON WARBLER AND PALO VERDI (Cock)
(Dendroica Auduboni)

Modeller: Dorothy Doughty
Height: 7 ½", 19.1 cm
Colour: Brownish-grey, yellow and white bird; yellow flowers; green stem; brown-grey base
Plinth: Wooden
Issued: 1963 in a limited edition of 500
Series: Doughty American Birds

Colourways	*Backstamp*	*U.S. $*	*Price* *Can. $*	*U.K. £*
Brownish-grey/yellow/white	Black	900.00	1,250.00	650.00

RW3670
AUDUBON WARBLER AND PALO VERDI (Hen)
(Dendroica Auduboni)

Modeller: Dorothy Doughty
Height: 7 ½", 19.1 cm
Colour: Brownish-grey, yellow and white bird; yellow flowers; green stem; brown-grey base
Plinth: Wooden
Issued: 1963 in a limited edition of 500
Series: Doughty American Birds

Colourways	*Backstamp*	*U.S. $*	*Price* *Can. $*	*U.K. £*
Brownish-grey/yellow/white	Black	900.00	1,250.00	650.00

RW3671
THE WINNER

Modeller: Doris Lindner
Height: 11 ¼", 28.5 cm
Colour: Rider: Red and purple silks; white jodhpurs; black hat and boots
Horse: Brown or grey
Plinth: Wooden
Issued: 1959-by 1980

Colourways	*Backstamp*	*U.S. $*	*Price Can. $*	*U.K. £*
Red/purple/white/bay	Black	1,500.00	1,800.00	800.00

Note: To make production more practical, the stable boy was eliminated from model RW3667 and the plinth was shortened slightly. Although the jockey came painted in the Queen's racing colours, for an extra fee, the colours could be customized.

RW3678
FOXHUNTER AND LIEUT.-COL. H.M. LLEWELLYN, C.B.E.

Modeller: Doris Lindner
Height: 12", 30.5 cm
Colour: Rider: Red jacket; white jodhpurs; black boots and hat
Horse: Bay with black lower legs and tail
Plinth: Wooden
Issued: 1959 in a limited edition of 500

Colourways	*Backstamp*	*U.S. $*	*Price Can. $*	*U.K. £*
Red/white/bay	Black	975.00	1,250.00	550.00

Note: There are 100 signed and 400 unsigned pieces.

RW3686
LARK SPARROW WITH TWIN POD AND RED GILA
(Chondestes Grammacus Striciatus)

Modeller: Dorothy Doughty
Height: 4 ½", 11.4 cm
Colour: Cream and brown bird; yellow and coral flowers; green leaves; dark grey-green base
Plinth: Wooden
Issued: 1966 in a limited edition of 500
Series: Doughty American Birds

Colourways	*Backstamp*	*U.S. $*	*Price Can. $*	*U.K. £*
Cream/brown/yellow/coral	Black	525.00	750.00	375.00

RW3689
JERSEY COW "BRAMLEY ZENORA"

Modeller: Doris Lindner
Height: 7 ¼", 18.4 cm
Colour: Light brown with black
Plinth: Wooden
Issued: 1959 in a limited edition of 500
Series: Prize Cattle

			Price	
Colourways	*Backstamp*	*U.S. $*	*Can. $*	*U.K. £*
Light brown	Black	1,000.00	1,300.00	600.00

RW3690
GREY WAGTAIL AND CELANDINE (Cock)
(Motacilla Melanope)

Modeller: Dorothy Doughty
Height: 6 ½", 16.5 cm
Colour: Light grey with yellow chest; green leaves; yellow flower
Plinth: Wooden
Issued: 1968 in a limited edition of 500
Series: Doughty British Birds

			Price	
Colourways	*Backstamp*	*U.S. $*	*Can. $*	*U.K. £*
Light grey/yellow	Black	525.00	750.00	375.00

RW3692
ENGLISH REDSTART ON GORSE IN SPRING (Cock)
(Ruticilla Phoenicurus)

Modeller: Dorothy Doughty
Height: 11 ¼", 28.5 cm
Colour: Grey with orange; yellow flowers; grey-green gorse
Plinth: Wooden
Issued: 1968 in a limited edition of 500
Series: Doughty British Birds

			Price	
Colourways	*Backstamp*	*U.S. $*	*Can. $*	*U.K. £*
Grey/orange/yellow/grey-green	Black	800.00	1,250.00	550.00

RW3693
ENGLISH REDSTART ON GORSE (Hen)
(Ruticilla Phoenicurus)

Modeller: Dorothy Doughty
Height: 7 ¾", 19.7 cm
Colour: Brown bird with red breast; green gorse; yellow flowers
Plinth: Wooden
Issued: 1968 in a limited edition of 500
Series: Doughty British Birds

			Price	
Colourways	*Backstamp*	*U.S. $*	*Can. $*	*U.K. £*
Brown/red	Black	750.00	1,000.00	550.00

RW3694
LESSER WHITETHROAT ON WILD ROSE (Cock)
(Sylvia Curruca)

Modeller: Dorothy Doughty
Height: 10 ¼", 26.0 cm
Colour: Unknown
Plinth: Wooden
Issued: 1966 in a limited edition of 500
Series: Doughty British Birds

			Price	
Colourways	*Backstamp*	*U.S. $*	*Can. $*	*U.K. £*
Unknown	Black	750.00	1,000.00	500.00

RW3695
LESSER WHITETHROAT ON WILD ROSE (Hen)
(Sylvia Curruca)

Modeller: Dorothy Doughty
Height: 10 ½", 26.7 cm
Colour: Unknown
Plinth: Wooden
Issued: 1966 in a limited edition of 500
Series: Doughty British Birds

			Price	
Colourways	*Backstamp*	*U.S. $*	*Can. $*	*U.K. £*
Unknown	Black	750.00	1,000.00	500.00

RW3696
WREN AND BURNET ROSE (Cock)
(Troglodytes Parvulus)

Modeller:	Dorothy Doughty
Height:	5 ¾", 14.6 cm
Colour:	Unknown
Plinth:	Wooden
Issued:	1966 in a limited edition of 500
Series:	Doughty British Birds

			Price	
Colourways	*Backstamp*	*U.S. $*	*Can. $*	*U.K. £*
Unknown	Black	950.00	1,350.00	650.00

RW3697
ABERDEEN ANGUS BULL "NEWHOUSE JEWLIAN ERIC"

Modeller:	Doris Lindner
Height:	7 ½", 19.1 cm
Colour:	Black
Plinth:	Wooden
Issued:	1959 in a limited edition of 500
Series:	Prized Cattle

			Price	
Colourways	*Backstamp*	*U.S. $*	*Can. $*	*U.K. £*
Black	Black	1,000.00	1,300.00	600.00

RW3701
NIGHTINGALE AND HONEYSUCKLE
(Daulias Luscinia)
Style One

Modeller:	Dorothy Doughty
Height:	10 ¼", 26.0 cm
Colour:	Russet brown and white bird; brown branch, pink flowers and green-grey leaves
Plinth:	Wooden
Issued:	1971 in a limited edition of 500
Series:	Doughty British Birds

			Price	
Colourways	*Backstamp*	*U.S. $*	*Can. $*	*U.K. £*
Brown/white/pink	Black	950.00	1,350.00	650.00

RW3702
SANTA GERTRUDIS BULL "PRINCE"

Modeller:	Doris Lindner
Height:	8 ¼", 20.9 cm
Colour:	Dark brown
Plinth:	Wooden
Issued:	1960 in a limited edition of 500
Series:	Prize Cattle

Colourways	*Backstamp*	*U.S. $*	*Price* *Can. $*	*U.K. £*
Dark brown	Black	1,000.00	1,300.00	600.00

RW3703
GOLDCREST AND LARCH (Cock)
(Regulus Cristatus)

Modeller:	Dorothy Doughty
Height:	10 ¼", 26.0 cm
Colour:	Unknown
Plinth:	Wooden
Issued:	1973 in a limited edition of 500
Series:	Doughty British Birds

Colourways	*Backstamp*	*U.S. $*	*Price* *Can. $*	*U.K. £*
Unknown	Black	850.00	1,200.00	600.00

RW3704
GOLDCREST AND LARCH (Hen)
(Regulus Cristatus)

Modeller:	Dorothy Doughty
Height:	10 ½", 26.6 cm
Colour:	Unknown
Plinth:	Wooden
Issued:	1973 in a limited edition of 500
Series:	Doughty British Birds

Colourways	*Backstamp*	*U.S. $*	*Price* *Can. $*	*U.K. £*
Unknown	Black	850.00	1,200.00	600.00

RW3707
ROBIN IN AUTUMN WOODS
(Erythacus Rebecula)

Modeller: Dorothy Doughty
Height: 7 ¼", 18.1 cm
Colour: Orange, browns and light blue; yellow mushrooms; green branches; brown rocks
Plinth: Wooden
Issued: 1966 in a limited edition of 500
Series: Doughty British Birds

			Price	
Colourways	*Backstamp*	*U.S. $*	*Can. $*	*U.K. £*
Orange/browns/blue	Black	675.00	950.00	475.00

RW3708
BLUE-TIT AND PUSSY WILLOW IN SPRING (Cock)
(Parus Coeruleus)

Modeller: Dorothy Doughty
Height: 7 ¾", 19.7 cm
Colour: Unknown
Plinth: Wooden
Issued: 1966 in a limited edition of 500
Series: Doughty British Birds

			Price	
Colourways	*Backstamp*	*U.S. $*	*Can. $*	*U.K. £*
Unknown	Black	850.00	1,150.00	575.00

RW3709
BLUE-TIT BATHING IN AN OLD WILLOW STUMP (Hen)

Modeller: Dorothy Doughty
Height: 6 ¾", 17.1 cm
Colour: Unknown
Plinth: Wooden
Issued: 1966 in a limited edition of 500
Series: Doughty British Birds

			Price	
Colourways	*Backstamp*	*U.S. $*	*Can. $*	*U.K. £*
Unknown	Black	850.00	1,150.00	575.00

RW3712
BULLFINCH AND BLACKTHORNE
(Pyrrhula Europoea)

Modeller:	Dorothy Doughty
Height:	Unknown
Colour:	Orange, black and grey bird; white flowers
Plinth:	Wooden
Issued:	1962 in a limited edition of 500
Series:	Doughty British Birds

Colourways	*Backstamp*	*U.S. $*	*Price* *Can. $*	*U.K. £*
Orange/grey	Black	775.00	1,100.00	550.00

RW3713
MEADOW PIPIT AND SILVERWEED (Cock)
(Anthus Pratensis)

Modeller:	Dorothy Doughty
Height:	6", 15.0 cm
Colour:	Yellow and light brown bird; yellow flowers; green fern leaves
Plinth:	Wooden
Issued:	1975 in a limited edition of 500
Series:	Doughty British Birds

Colourways	*Backstamp*	*U.S. $*	*Price* *Can. $*	*U.K. £*
Yellow/light brown	Black	550.00	800.00	400.00

RW3719
ARAB STALLION "INDIAN MAGIC"

Modeller:	Doris Lindner
Height:	10", 25.4 cm
Colour:	1. Dappled 2. White
Plinth:	Wooden
Issued:	1961 in a limited edition of 500

Colourways	*Backstamp*	*U.S. $*	*Price* *Can. $*	*U.K. £*
1. Coloured (as above)	Black	1,000.00	1,500.00	600.00
2. White	Black	350.00	500.00	200.00

RW3721
SAIL FISH

Modeller: Ronald Van Ruyckevelt
Height: 8 ½", 21.6 cm
Colour: Blue and white
Plinth: Wooden
Issued: 1961 in a limited edition of 500
Series: Sporting Fish

Colourways	*Backstamp*	*Price* *U.S. $*	*Can. $*	*U.K. £*
Blue/white	Black	650.00	900.00	450.00

RW3722
FLYING FISH

Modeller: Ronald Van Ruyckevelt
Height: 8 ½", 21.6 cm
Colour: Blue, green and white
Plinth: Wooden
Issued: 1961 in a limited edition of 500
Series: Sporting Fish

Colourways	*Backstamp*	*Price* *U.S. $*	*Can. $*	*U.K. £*
Blue/green/white	Black	775.00	1,100.00	550.00

RW3723
CHIFFCHAFF ON HOGWEED
(Phylloscopus Rufus)

Modeller: Dorothy Doughty
Height: 17 ¾", 45.1 cm
Colour: Yellow bird; green foliage
Plinth: Wooden
Issued: 1966 in a limited edition of 500
Series: Doughty British Birds

Colourways	*Backstamp*	*Price* *U.S. $*	*Can. $*	*U.K. £*
Yellow/green	Black	1,150.00	1,500.00	800.00

RW3726
MOORHEN CHICK ON WATERLILY PADS
(Gallinula Chloropus)

Modeller: Dorothy Doughty
Height: 3 ¾", 9.5 cm
Colour: Black bird with yellow beak; white lily; green leaves
Issued: 1970 in a limited edition of 500
Series: Doughty British Birds

			Price	
Colourways	*Backstamp*	*U.S. $*	*Can. $*	*U.K. £*
Black/white/green	Black	650.00	900.00	450.00

RW3727
WREN AND BURNET ROSE (Hen)
(Troglodytes Parvulus)

Modeller: Dorothy Doughty
Height: 7 ¼", 19.7 cm
Colour: Unknown
Plinth: Wooden
Issued: 1966 in a limited edition of 500
Series: Doughty British Birds

			Price	
Colourways	*Backstamp*	*U.S. $*	*Can. $*	*U.K. £*
Unknown	Black	900.00	1,250.00	650.00

Photograph not available at press time

RW3731
RED ADMIRAL BUTTERFLY ON CLEMATIS

Modeller: Peter Ewence
Height: Unknown
Colour: Unknown
Issued: 1962

			Price	
Colourways	*Backstamp*	*U.S. $*	*Can. $*	*U.K. £*
Unknown	Black		Rare	

RW3733
AMERICAN QUARTER HORSE "POCO STAMPEDE"

Modeller: Doris Lindner
Height: 9 ½", 24.0 cm
Colour: Light chestnut with black tail and lower legs
Plinth: Wooden
Issued: 1962 in a limited edition of 500

Colourways	*Backstamp*	*U.S. $*	*Price Can. $*	*U.K. £*
Chestnut/black	Black	1,000.00	1,350.00	600.00

RW3734
KINGFISHER AND AUTUMN BEECH (Cock)
(Alcedo Ispida)

Modeller: Dorothy Doughty
Height: 12 ¼", 31.1 cm
Colour: Blue, green and brown; gold leaves
Plinth: Wooden
Issued: 1966 in a limited edition of 500
Series: Doughty British Birds

Colourways	*Backstamp*	*U.S. $*	*Price Can. $*	*U.K. £*
Green/grey	Black	775.00	1,100.00	550.00

RW3735
LONG-TAILED TITS ON FLOWERING LARCH
(Acredula Caudata)

Modeller: Dorothy Doughty
Height: Unknown
Colour: Unknown
Issued: 1962 in a limited edition of 500
Series: Doughty British Birds

Colourways	*Backstamp*	*U.S. $*	*Price Can. $*	*U.K. £*
Unknown	Black	Not put into full production		

RW3745
MERANO AND CAP. RAIMONDO D'INZEO

Modeller: Doris Lindner
Height: 11", 27.9 cm
Colour: Rider: Olive jacket and cap; white jodhpurs; black boots
Horse: Chestnut
Plinth: Wooden
Issued: 1962 in a limited edition of 500

			Price	
Colourways	*Backstamp*	*U.S. $*	*Can. $*	*U.K. £*
Olive/white/chestnut	Black	1,200.00	1,675.00	750.00

RW3746
BRITISH FRIESIAN BULL "TERLING TRUSTY"

Modeller: Doris Lindner
Height: 8 ½", 21.6 cm
Colour: Black and white
Plinth: Wooden
Issued: 1962 in a limited edition of 500
Series: Prize Cattle

			Price	
Colourways	*Backstamp*	*U.S. $*	*Can. $*	*U.K. £*
Black/white	Black	1,250.00	1,650.00	700.00

RW3751
TARPON

Modeller: Ronald Van Ruyckevelt
Height: 12", 30.5 cm
Colour: White, grey and black
Plinth: Wooden
Issued: 1962 in a limited edition of 500
Series: Sporting Fish

			Price	
Colourways	*Backstamp*	*U.S. $*	*Can. $*	*U.K. £*
White/grey/black	Black	650.00	900.00	450.00

RW3753
DOLPHIN

Modeller: Ronald Van Ruyckevelt
Height: 10 ½", 26.7 cm
Colour: Turquoise and cream
Plinth: Wooden
Issued: 1962 in a limited edition of 500
Series: Sporting Fish

Colourways	*Backstamp*	*U.S. $*	*Price* *Can. $*	*U.K. £*
Turquoise/cream	Black	650.00	900.00	450.00

RW3758
HYPERION

Modeller: Doris Lindner
Height: 10", 25.4 cm
Colour: Brown with white socks
Plinth: Wooden
Issued: 1963 in a limited edition of 500

Colourways	*Backstamp*	*U.S. $*	*Price* *Can. $*	*U.K. £*
Brown	Black	950.00	1,350.00	600.00

RW3759
SHIRE STALLION "MANOR PREMIER KING"

Modeller: Doris Lindner
Height: 10 ½", 26.7 cm
Colour: Brown with black and white socks
Plinth: Wooden
Issued: 1963 in a limited edition of 500
Series: Heavy Horses

Colourways	*Backstamp*	*U.S. $*	*Price* *Can. $*	*U.K. £*
Brown/black/white	Black	950.00	1,350.00	600.00

RW3776
JERSEY BULL "LEEBARN CARLISLE II"

Modeller: Doris Lindner
Height: 7 ¼", 18.4 cm
Colour: Light brown and black
Plinth: Wooden
Issued: 1964 in a limited edition of 500
Series: Prize Cattle

			Price	
Colourways	***Backstamp***	***U.S. $***	***Can. $***	***U.K. £***
Light brown/black	Black	1,000.00	1,300.00	600.00

RW3778
BLUE MARLIN

Modeller: Ronald Van Ruyckevelt
Height: 11 ½", 29.2 cm
Colour: Blue and white
Plinth: Wooden
Issued: 1964 in a limited edition of 500
Series: Sporting Fish

			Price	
Colourways	***Backstamp***	***U.S. $***	***Can. $***	***U.K. £***
Blue/white	Black	625.00	900.00	450.00

RW3781
DAIRY SHORTHORN BULL "ROYAL EVENT"

Modeller: Doris Lindner
Height: 8", 20.3 cm
Colour: Browns and white
Plinth: Wooden
Issued: 1964 in a limited edition of 500
Series: Prize Cattle

			Price	
Colourways	***Backstamp***	***U.S. $***	***Can. $***	***U.K. £***
Browns/white	Black	1,000.00	1,300.00	600.00

RW3786
PERCHERON STALLION "SALTMARSH SILVER CREST"

Modeller: Doris Lindner
Height: 10", 25.4 cm
Colour: Iron grey
Plinth: Wooden
Issued: 1965 in a limited edition of 500
Series: Heavy Horses

			Price	
Colourways	*Backstamp*	*U.S. $*	*Can. $*	*U.K. £*
Unknown	Black	950.00	1,350.00	600.00

RW3787
BLUE-FIN TUNA

Modeller: Ronald Van Ruyckevelt
Height: 11 ½", 29.2 cm
Colour: Blue
Plinth: Wooden
Issued: 1965 in a limited edition of 500
Series: Sporting Fish

			Price	
Colourways	*Backstamp*	*U.S. $*	*Can. $*	*U.K. £*
Blue	Black	650.00	900.00	450.00

RW3788
SWORDFISH

Modeller: Ronald Van Ruyckevelt
Height: 14 ½", 36.8 cm
Colour: Unknown
Plinth: Wooden
Issued: 1965 in a limited edition of 500
Series: Sporting Fish

			Price	
Colourways	*Backstamp*	*U.S. $*	*Can. $*	*U.K. £*
Unknown	Black	650.00	900.00	450.00

Photograph not available at press time

RW3789
AMERICAN SALMON

Modeller: Ronald Van Ruyckevelt
Height: Unknown
Colour: Unknown
Issued: 1965

Colourways	Backstamp	Price U.S. $	Price Can. $	Price U.K. £
Unknown	Black	Not put into full production		

RW3790
AMERICAN TROUT

Modeller: Ronald Van Ruyckevelt
Height: Unknown
Colour: Unknown
Issued: 1965

Colourways	Backstamp	Price U.S. $	Price Can. $	Price U.K. £
Unknown	Black	Not put into full production		

Photograph not available at press time

RW3802
WELSH MOUNTAIN PONY "COED COCH PLANED"

Modeller: Doris Lindner
Height: 8", 20.3 cm
Colour: White
Plinth: Wooden
Issued: 1965 in a limited edition of 500

Colourways	Backstamp	Price U.S. $	Price Can. $	Price U.K. £
White	Black	1,000.00	1,300.00	600.00

RW3805
ROYAL CANADIAN MOUNTED POLICE

Modeller: Doris Lindner
Height: 12 ¼", 31.1 cm
Colour: Red jacket; black trousers; brown hat and boots; black horse
Plinth: Wooden
Issued: 1967 in a limited edition of 500

Description	*Backstamp*	*Price U.S. $*	*Can. $*	*U.K. £*
1. With 1967 symbol	Black	2,000.00	2,750.00	1,200.00
2. Without 1967 symbol	Black	2,000.00	2,750.00	1,200.00

Note: The first 100 models issued bore the Canadian Centennial Symbol for 1967.

RW3808
ARAB STALLION'S HEAD

Modeller: Raoh Schorr
Height: 12 ¼", 31.1 cm
Colour: White porcelain
Issued: 1966

Colourways	*Backstamp*	*Price U.S. $*	*Can. $*	*U.K. £*
White	Black	Trial models only		

RW3811
FAWN'S HEAD (Vase)

Modeller: Raoh Schorr
Height: 12", 30.5 cm
Colour: White porcelain
Issued: 1966

Colourways	*Backstamp*	*Price U.S. $*	*Can. $*	*U.K. £*
White	Black	375.00	500.00	250.00

Photograph not available at press time

RW3812
HORSE'S HEAD (Vase)

Modeller: Raoh Schorr
Height: 12", 30.5 cm
Colour: White porcelain
Issued: 1966

			Price	
Colourways	*Backstamp*	*U.S. $*	*Can. $*	*U.K. £*
White	Black	375.00	500.00	250.00

RW3813
MALLARD (Drake)

Modeller: Ronald Van Ruyckevelt
Height: 12", 30.5 cm
Colour: White, brown and green
Plinth: Wooden
Issued: 1966 in a limited edition of 500
Series: Game Birds

			Price	
Colourways	*Backstamp*	*U.S. $*	*Can. $*	*U.K. £*
White/brown/green	Black	650.00	900.00	450.00

RW3814
MALLARD (Hen)

Modeller: Ronald Van Ruyckevelt
Height: 13 ½", 34.3 cm
Colour: Browns and green
Plinth: Wooden
Issued: 1966 in a limited edition of 500
Series: Game Birds

			Price	
Colourways	*Backstamp*	*U.S. $*	*Can. $*	*U.K. £*
Browns/green	Black	650.00	900.00	450.00

RW3815
MONKEY (Two feet on ground)

Modeller: Raoh Schorr
Height: Unknown
Colour: White porcelain
Issued: 1966

Colourways	Backstamp	Price U.S. $	Can. $	U.K. £
White	Black	Trial models only		

RW3816
MONKEY (Four feet on ground)

Modeller: Raoh Schorr
Height: Unknown
Colour: White porcelain
Issued: 1966

Colourways	Backstamp	Price U.S. $	Can. $	U.K. £
White	Black	Trial models only		

RW3817
ARKLE

Modeller: Doris Lindner
Height: 10 ¼", 26.0 cm
Colour: Chestnut and black
Plinth: Wooden
Issued: 1966 in a limited edition of 500
Series: Race Horses

Colourways	Backstamp	Price U.S. $	Can. $	U.K. £
Chestnut/black	Black	1,200.00	1,750.00	850.00

RW3818
RING-NECKED PHEASANT (Cock)

Modeller: Ronald Van Ruyckevelt
Height: 13 ¾", 34.9 cm
Colour: Black head with red eye patch; reddish-brown and yellow body; white stripe around neck
Plinth: Wooden
Issued: 1966 in a limited edition of 500
Series: Game Birds

Colourways	Backstamp	U.S. $	Price Can. $	U.K. £
Black/red/brown/yellow	Black	650.00	900.00	450.00

RW3819
RING-NECKED PHEASANT (Hen)

Modeller: Ronald Van Ruyckevelt
Height: 12 ¾", 32.4 cm
Colour: Browns and green
Plinth: Wooden
Issued: 1966 in a limited edition of 500
Series: Game Birds

Colourways	Backstamp	U.S. $	Price Can. $	U.K. £
Browns/green	Black	650.00	900.00	450.00

RW3821
BRAHMAN BULL "J. D. H. DE ELLARY MANSO"

Modeller: Doris Lindner
Height: 8 ¾", 22.2 cm
Colour: White and black
Plinth: Wooden
Issued: 1967 in a limited edition of 500
Series: Prize Cattle

Colourways	Backstamp	U.S. $	Price Can. $	U.K. £
White/black	Black	1,000.00	1,300.00	600.00

RW3822
BULLDOG "MACK"

Modeller: Doris Lindner
Height: 8 ½", 21.6 cm
Colour: Brown and white
Plinth: Wooden
Issued: 1967 in a limited edition of 500

Colourways	*Backstamp*	*U.S. $*	*Price Can. $*	*U.K. £*
Brown/white	Black	750.00	1,000.00	500.00

Note: Commissioned by Mack Trucks Inc., USA.

RW3824
CHAROLAIS BULL "VAILLANT"

Modeller: Doris Lindner
Height: 8", 20.3 cm
Colour: Cream
Plinth: Wooden
Issued: 1967 in a limited edition of 500
Series: Prize Cattle

Colourways	*Backstamp*	*U.S. $*	*Price Can. $*	*U.K. £*
Cream	Black	1,000.00	1,300.00	600.00

RW3825
SUFFOLK PUNCH "BECCLES WARRENDER"

Modeller: Doris Lindner
Height: 9 ¼", 23.5 cm
Colour: Chestnut
Plinth: Wooden
Issued: 1967 in a limited edition of 500
Series: Heavy Horses

Colourways	*Backstamp*	*U.S. $*	*Price Can. $*	*U.K. £*
Chestnut	Black	1,500.00	1,750.00	900.00

RW3827
BOB-WHITE QUAIL (Cock)
Style Two

Modeller: Ronald Van Ruyckevelt
Height: 9 ¼", 23.5 cm
Colour: Dark brown, cream and green
Plinth: Wooden
Issued: 1967 in a limited edition of 500
Series: Game Birds

Colourways	*Backstamp*	*U.S. $*	*Price* *Can. $*	*U.K. £*
Dark brown/cream/green	Black	650.00	900.00	450.00

RW3828
BOB-WHITE QUAIL (Hen)
Style Two

Modeller: Ronald Van Ruyckevelt
Height: 7", 17.8 cm
Colour: Browns, black, white and green
Plinth: Wooden
Issued: 1967 in a limited edition of 500
Series: Game Birds

Colourways	*Backstamp*	*U.S. $*	*Price* *Can. $*	*U.K. £*
Browns/black/white	Black	650.00	900.00	450.00

RW3831
CANVASBACK DUCK

Modeller: Ronald Van Ruyckevelt
Height: 16 ½", 41.9 cm
Colour: Black, brown, grey and green
Plinth: Wooden
Issued: 1967 in a limited edition of 500
Series: Game Birds

Colourways	*Backstamp*	*U.S. $*	*Price* *Can. $*	*U.K. £*
Black/white/grey/green	Black	650.00	900.00	450.00

RW3833
PINTAIL (Drake)

Modeller: Ronald Van Ruyckevelt
Height: 7 ½", 19.1 cm
Colour: Grey, green, brown and white
Plinth: Wooden
Issued: 1967 in a limited edition of 500
Series: Game Birds

Colourways	*Backstamp*	*U.S. $*	*Price* *Can. $*	*U.K. £*
Grey/green/brown/white	Black	650.00	900.00	450.00

RW3834
PINTAIL (Hen)

Modeller: Ronald Van Ruyckevelt
Height: 13 ½", 34.3 cm
Colour: Cream and light green
Plinth: Wooden
Issued: 1967 in a limited edition of 500
Series: Game Birds

Colourways	*Backstamp*	*U.S. $*	*Price* *Can. $*	*U.K. £*
Cream/light green	Black	650.00	900.00	450.00

RW3836
GREEN-WINGED TEAL

Modeller: Ronald Van Ruyckevelt
Height: 8 ¾", 22.2 cm
Colour: Grey, white and yellow
Plinth: Wooden
Issued: 1967 in a limited edition of 500
Series: Game Birds

Colourways	*Backstamp*	*U.S. $*	*Price* *Can. $*	*U.K. £*
Grey/white/yellow	Black	650.00	900.00	450.00

RW3840
MOURNING DOVES

Modeller: Ronald Van Ruyckevelt
Height: 17 ¾", 45.1 cm
Colour: Browns
Plinth: Wooden, tall
Issued: 1967 limited edition of 500

Colourways	Backstamp	U.S. $	Price Can. $	U.K. £
Browns	Black	1,150.00	1,600.00	800.00

RW3844
PUFFIN

Modeller: Raoh Schorr
Height: Unknown
Colour: White, black and orange (porcelain)
Issued: 1967

Colourways	Backstamp	U.S. $	Price Can. $	U.K. £
White/black/orange	Black	650.00	900.00	450.00

RW3845
FULMAR

Modeller: Raoh Schorr
Height: Unknown
Colour: Grey and white; yellow beak (porcelain)
Issued: 1967

Colourways	Backstamp	U.S. $	Price Can. $	U.K. £
Grey/white	Black	650.00	900.00	450.00

RW3846
H.R.H. THE DUKE OF EDINBURGH ON HIS POLO PONY

Modeller: Doris Lindner
Height: 15 ¾", 40.0 cm
Colour: Dark grey shirt; white jodhpurs; black hat; bay horse
Plinth: Wooden
Issued: 1968 in a limited edition of 750

Colourways	*Backstamp*	*U.S. $*	*Price* *Can. $*	*U.K. £*
Dark grey/white/black	Black	1,125.00	1,450.00	650.00

RW3860
NAPOLEON BONAPARTE

Modeller: Bernard Winskill
Height: 16 ¼", 41.2 cm
Colour: 1. Bone china: Red cape; dark blue coat, hat, boots and saddlecloth; cream breeches and gloves; white horse; gold reins
2. Bronze metal
Plinth: Wooden
Issued: 1. Bone china: 1968 in a limited edition of 750
2. Bronze metal: 1968 in a limited edition of 15
Series: Military Commanders

Description	*Backstamp*	*U.S. $*	*Price* *Can. $*	*U.K. £*
1. Bone china	Black	3,500.00	4,500.00	2,000.00
2. Bronze metal	R-W	6,000.00	8,000.00	3,500.00

RW3869
APPALOOSA "IMBODEN'S DRIFTWOOD BOB"

Modeller: Doris Lindner
Height: 9 ¾", 24.7 cm
Colour: White and brown
Plinth: Wooden
Issued: 1968 in a limited edition of 750

Colourways	*Backstamp*	*U.S. $*	*Price* *Can. $*	*U.K. £*
White/brown	Black	1,000.00	1,300.00	600.00

RW3870
THE DUKE OF WELLINGTON

Modeller: Bernard Winskill
Height: 16", 40.6 cm
Colour: 1. Bone china: Rider: Red jacket with blue sash; white jodhpurs; black boots; Horse: Brown
2. Bronze metal
Plinth: Wooden
Issued: 1. Bone china: 1968 in a limited edition of 750
2. Bronze metal: 1968 in a limited edition of 15
Series: Military Commanders

Description	*Backstamp*	*U.S. $*	*Price Can. $*	*U.K. £*
1. Bone china	Black	4,000.00	5,000.00	2,300.00
2. Bronze metal	R-W	6,000.00	8,000.00	3,500.00

RW3871
PRINCE'S GRACE AND FOAL

Modeller: Doris Lindner
Height: 8 ¾", 22.2 cm
Colour: 1. Coloured (with wooden plinth)
2. White (Classic, without plinth)
Issued: 1. Coloured: 1968 in a limited edition of 750
2. White: 1968 in a limited edition of 250

Colourways	*Backstamp*	*U.S. $*	*Price Can. $*	*U.K. £*
1. Coloured	Black	900.00	1,350.00	600.00
2. White	Gold	300.00	400.00	200.00

RW3872
STROLLER AND MARION COAKES

Modeller: Doris Lindner
Height: 11 ¼", 28.5 cm
Colour: Rider: Black jacket and boots; white jodhpurs
Horse: Light brown
Plinth: Wooden
Issued: 1968 in a limited edition of 750

Colourways	*Backstamp*	*U.S. $*	*Price Can. $*	*U.K. £*
Black/white/brown	Black	950.00	1,350.00	600.00

Note: Only trial pieces are known for the following models: RW3873 Baltimore Oriole; RW3874 Purple Thrush; RW3875 Americal Goldfinch, RW3876 Nashville Warbler.

WILDLIFE

RW4272 Peregrine Falcon, Style One

RW3617 Elf Owl and Saguaro

RW3813 Mallard (Drake)

RW3814 Mallard (Hen)

BIRDS AND ANIMALS ON BRONZE

RW4180 Red Cardinal on Bronze

RW4179 Robin and Narcissus

RW3898 Kingfisher on Bronze, Style One

RW3900 Wren on Bronze, Style One

RW4241 Barn Owl

RW4212 Hedgehog on Bronze, Style Two

BIRDS

RW2843 Duck

RW3913 White Doves

RW3981 Kek (Kestrel)

RW4056 Marsh Tit on Daphne

RW3921 Rainbow Lorikeet on Red Flowered Gum

RW3961 Bearded Reedling

HORSES WITH RIDERS

RW3116 Over the Sticks

RW3912 H.R.H. Princess Anne and Doublet

RW3846 H.R.H. The Duke of Edinburgh on His Polo Pony

RW3166 Highwayman

HORSES

RW3893 Nijinsky

RW3758 Hyperion

RW3957 New Born (Classic)

RW4096 Hunter

DOGS

RW2934 Sealyham Terrier (Without plinth)

RW2931 Bull Terrier "Bill"

RW3133 Bulldog Puppies (Two)

RW3132 Foxhound Puppies (Three)

DOGS

RW4081 Old English Sheepdog Puppy (Playing)

RW4036 Labrador (Seated)

RW4035 Boxer (Seated)

RW4010 Red Setter (Lying on base)

MISCELLANEOUS

RW3093 Penguin (Head forward)

RW3096 Elephant (Style One)

RW3131 Young Foxes (Three)

RW3123 Maytime (With base)

RW3880
AMERICAN SADDLE HORSE

Modeller: Doris Lindner
Height: 10 ¼", 26.0 cm
Colour: Brown
Plinth: Wooden
Issued: 1971 in a limited edition of 500

Colourways	*Backstamp*	*Price U.S. $*	*Can. $*	*U.K. £*
Brown	Black	1,250.00	1,700.00	750.00

RW3882
PALOMINO "YELLOW STRAW"

Modeller: Doris Lindner
Height: 10 ¼", 26.0 cm
Colour: Palomino
Plinth: Wooden
Issued: 1971 in a limited edition of 750

Colourways	*Backstamp*	*Price U.S. $*	*Can. $*	*U.K. £*
Palomino	Black	950.00	1,350.00	600.00

Note: Only trial pieces are known for the following models: RW3885 Chickadee; RW3886 Wren.

RW3893
NIJINSKY

Modeller: Doris Lindner
Height: 10 ¼", 26.0 cm
Colour: Tawny
Plinth: Wooden
Issued: 1971 in a limited edition of 500
Series: Race Horses

Colourways	*Backstamp*	*Price U.S. $*	*Can. $*	*U.K. £*
Tawny	Black	1,250.00	1,700.00	850.00

RW3894
SPARROWHAWK AND BULLFINCH

Modeller:	James Alder
Height:	1. Bone china: 22", 55.9 cm 2. Bronze: 25 ½", 64.8 cm
Colour:	1A. Bone china: White 1B. Bone china: Yellow and grey; grey and brown 2. Bronze
Plinth:	Wooden
Issued:	1A. White: 1969 in a limited edition of 150 1B. Coloured: 1969 in a limited edition of 250 2. Bronze: 1969 in a limited edition of 25

Colourways	*Backstamp*	*U.S. $*	*Price Can. $*	*U.K. £*
1A. White	Black	500.00	700.00	350.00
1B. Yellow/grey/brown	Black	1,000.00	1,500.00	750.00
2. Bronze	R-W	1,500.00	2,000.00	1,000.00

RW3897
WASHINGTON (George)

Modeller:	Bernard Winskill
Height:	18", 45.7 cm
Colour:	1. Bone china: Navy jacket with gold trim; black boots; white jodhpurs; grey horse 2. Bronze metal
Plinth:	Wooden
Issued:	1. Bone china: 1972 in a limited edition of 750 2. Bronze metal: 1975 in a limited edition of 15
Series:	Military Commanders

Description	*Backstamp*	*U.S. $*	*Price Can. $*	*U.K. £*
1. Bone china	Black	4,000.00	5,000.00	2,300.00
2. Bronze metal	R-W	6,000.00	8,000.00	3,500.00

RW3898
KINGFISHER ON BRONZE
Style One

Modeller:	David Fryer
Height:	7", 17.8 cm
Colour:	Blue and orange bird; yellow flower; bronze foliage and base
Issued:	1984-1988
Series:	British Birds on Bronze (Small size)

Colourways	*Backstamp*	*U.S. $*	*Price Can. $*	*U.K. £*
Blue/orange/yellow/bronze	R-W	125.00	175.00	95.00

RW3899
SWALLOW ON BRONZE

Modeller: David Fryer
Height: 5 ½", 14.0 cm
Colour: Black, white and red bird; pink flowers; bronze foliage and base
Issued: 1984-1988
Series: British Birds on Bronze (Small size)

Colourways	*Backstamp*	*U.S. $*	*Price Can. $*	*U.K. £*
Black/white/red/pink/bronze	R-W	125.00	175.00	95.00

RW3900
WREN ON BRONZE
Style One

Modeller: David Fryer
Height: 4 ½", 11.9 cm
Colour: Brown bird; pink flowers; bronze foliage and base
Issued: 1984-1988
Series: British Birds on Bronze (Small size)

Colourways	*Backstamp*	*U.S. $*	*Price Can. $*	*U.K. £*
Brown/pink/bronze	R-W	125.00	175.00	95.00

RW3901
ROBIN ON BRONZE
Style One

Modeller: David Fryer
Height: 6 ¾", 17.2 cm
Colour: Red and brown bird, white and yellow flowers; bronze foliage and base
Issued: 1984-1988
Series: British Birds on Bronze (Small size)

Colourways	*Backstamp*	*U.S. $*	*Price Can. $*	*U.K. £*
Red/brown/white/yellow	R-W	125.00	175.00	95.00

RW3902
GOLDCREST ON BRONZE
Style Two

Modeller: David Fryer
Height: 4", 10.1 cm
Colour: Yellow, green and brown bird; brown acorns; bronze foliage and base
Issued: 1984-1988
Series: British Birds on Bronze (Small size)

Colourways	*Backstamp*	*U.S. $*	*Price Can. $*	*U.K. £*
Yellow/green/brown/bronze	R-W	125.00	175.00	95.00

RW3903
BLUE TIT ON BRONZE
Style Two

Modeller: David Fryer
Height: 5", 12.7 cm
Colour: Blue, green and white bird; yellow flowers; bronze foliage and base
Issued: 1984-1988
Series: British Birds on Bronze (Small size)

Colourways	*Backstamp*	*U.S. $*	*Price Can. $*	*U.K. £*
Blue/green/white/yellow	R-W	125.00	175.00	95.00

Photograph not available at press time

RW3904
KINGFISHER ON BRONZE (Domed)
Style Two

Modeller: David Fryer
Height: 3", 7.6 cm
Colour: Blue and orange bird; bronze foliage
Issued: 1984
Series: British Birds on Bronze (Miniature)

Colourways	*Backstamp*	*U.S. $*	*Price Can. $*	*U.K. £*
Blue/orange/bronze	R-W	90.00	125.00	65.00

Note: Model RW3904 was issued with a wooden plinth and glass dome (4").

RW3905
ROBIN ON BRONZE (Domed)
Style Two

Modeller: David Fryer
Height: 3", 7.6 cm
Colour: Brown and red bird; bronze foliage
Issued: 1984
Series: British Birds on Bronze (Miniature)

Colourways	*Backstamp*	*U.S. $*	*Price* *Can. $*	*U.K. £*
Brown/red/bronze	R-W	90.00	125.00	65.00

Note: Model RW3905 was issued with a wooden plinth and glass dome (4").

Photograph not available at press time

Photograph not available at press time

RW3907
NUTHATCH ON BRONZE (Domed)

Modeller: David Fryer
Height: 3", 7.6 cm
Colour: Unknown
Issued: 1984
Series: British Birds on Bronze (Miniature)

Colourways	*Backstamp*	*U.S. $*	*Price* *Can. $*	*U.K. £*
Unknown	R-W	90.00	125.00	65.00

Note: Model RW3907 was issued with a wooden plinth and glass dome (4").

RW3908
BLUE TIT ON BRONZE (Domed)
Style Three

Modeller: David Fryer
Height: 3", 7.6 cm
Colour: Blue bird; bronze foliage and base
Issued: 1984
Series: British Birds on Bronze (Miniature)

Colourways	*Backstamp*	*U.S. $*	*Price* *Can. $*	*U.K. £*
Blue/bronze	R-W	90.00	125.00	65.00

Note: Model RW3908 was issued with a wooden plinth and glass dome (4").

Photograph not available at press time

Photograph not available at press time

RW3909
GOLDCREST ON BRONZE (Domed)
Style Three

Modeller: David Fryer
Height: 3″, 7.6 cm
Colour: Unknown
Issued: 1984
Series: British Birds on Bronze (Miniature)

Colourways	*Backstamp*	*U.S. $*	*Price* *Can. $*	*U.K. £*
Unknown	R-W	90.00	125.00	65.00

Note: Model RW3909 was issued with a wooden plinth and glass dome (4″).

RW3910
WREN ON BRONZE (Domed)
Style Two

Modeller: David Fryer
Height: 3″, 7.6 cm
Colour: Brown bird; bronze foliage and base
Issued: 1984
Series: British Birds on Bronze (Miniature)

Colourways	*Backstamp*	*U.S. $*	*Price* *Can. $*	*U.K. £*
Brown/bronze	R-W	90.00	125.00	65.00

Note: Model RW3910 was issued with a wooden plinth and glass dome (4″).

Photograph not available at press time

Photograph not available at press time

RW3911
MERLIN HAWK ON BRONZE

Modeller: David Fryer
Height: Unknown
Colour: Unknown
Issued: 1984
Series: British Birds on Bronze (Large size)

Colourways	*Backstamp*	*U.S. $*	*Price* *Can. $*	*U.K. £*
Unknown	R-W		Rare	

RW3912
H.R.H. PRINCESS ANNE AND DOUBLET

Modeller: Doris Lindner
Height: 13", 33.0 cm
Colour: Rider: Blue jersey; cream jodhpurs; black hat
Horse: Brown
Plinth: Wooden
Issued: 1972 in a limited edition of 750

Colourways	*Backstamp*	*Price* *U.S. $*	*Can. $*	*U.K. £*
Blue/cream/brown	Black	1,225.00	1,575.00	700.00

RW3913
WHITE DOVES

Modeller: Ronald Van Ruyckevelt
Height: 18", 45.7 cm
Colour: White
Plinth: Wooden
Issued: 1972 in a limited edition of 25

Colourways	*Backstamp*	*Price* *U.S. $*	*Can. $*	*U.K. £*
White	Black	1,350.00	1,950.00	950.00

Note: White Doves, model RW3913, was issued to commemorate the Silver Wedding Anniversary of HM Queen Elizabeth II and the Duke of Edinburgh.

RW3914
THE DUKE OF MARLBOROUGH

Modeller: Bernard Winskill
Height: 18", 45.7 cm
Colour: 1. Bone china: Red jacket; blue sash and trim; grey horse
2. Bronze metal
Plinth: Wooden
Issued: 1. Bone china: 1973 in a limited edition of 350
2. Bronze metal: 1973 in a limited edition of 15
Series: Military Commanders

Description	*Backstamp*	*Price* *U.S. $*	*Can. $*	*U.K. £*
1. Bone china	Black	3,500.00	4,500.00	2,000.00
2. Bronze metal	R-W	6,000.00	8,000.00	3,500.00

RW3921
RAINBOW LORIKEET ON RED FLOWERED GUM

Modeller: James Alder
Height: 20 ½", 52.1 cm
Colour: Red, yellow, blue and green bird; green leaves; brown eucalyptus branch with green leaves
Plinth: Wooden
Issued: 1972 in a limited edition of 50

Colourways	*Backstamp*	*U.S. $*	*Price Can. $*	*U.K. £*
Red/yellow/blue/green	Black	1,200.00	1,750.00	850.00

RW3922
GALLOPING DARTMOOR PONIES

Modeller: Doris Lindner
Height: 8 ¾", 22.2 cm
Colour: 1. Brown and black
2. White
Plinth: Wooden
Issued: 1. Coloured: 1972 in a limited edition of 500
2. White: 1972 in a limited edition of 250

Colourways	*Backstamp*	*U.S. $*	*Price Can. $*	*U.K. £*
1. Brown/black	Black	1,500.00	1,850.00	975.00
2. White	Black	500.00	750.00	350.00

RW3935
HACKNEY STALLION

Modeller: Doris Lindner
Height: 11", 27.9 cm
Colour: Brown with black shading
Plinth: Wooden
Issued: 1973 in a limited edition of 500

Colourways	*Backstamp*	*U.S. $*	*Price Can. $*	*U.K. £*
Brown/black	Black	1,250.00	1,500.00	850.00

RW3942
MILL REEF

Modeller:	Doris Lindner
Height:	11 ½", 29.2 cm
Colour:	Chestnut
Plinth:	Wooden
Issued:	1973 in a limited edition of 500
Series:	Race Horses

Colourways	*Backstamp*	*Price* *U.S. $*	*Can. $*	*U.K. £*
Chestnut	Black	1,200.00	1,700.00	850.00

RW3943
RICHARD MEADE AND LAURISTON

Modeller:	Doris Lindner
Height:	13", 33.0 cm
Colour:	Rider: Cream riding outfit; black hat Horse: Black
Plinth:	Wooden
Issued:	1974 in a limited edition of 500

Colourways	*Backstamp*	*Price* *U.S. $*	*Can. $*	*U.K. £*
Cream/black	Black	950.00	1,350.00	600.00

RW3944
CLYDESDALE STALLION

Modeller:	Doris Lindner
Height:	10 ¾", 27.3 cm
Colour:	1. Light chestnut with white feathers 2. Light tan with white feathers
Plinth:	Wooden
Issued:	1975 in a limited edition of 500
Series:	Heavy Horses

Colourways	*Backstamp*	*Price* *U.S. $*	*Can. $*	*U.K. £*
Coloured (as above)	Black	950.00	1,350.00	600.00

RW3948
BY A SHORT HEAD

Modeller:	Bernard Winskill
Height:	Unknown
Colour:	1. Bone china: Rider One: Yellow and white silks; Rider Two: Blue and white silks Horses: Chestnut 2. Bronze metal
Plinth:	Wooden
Issued:	1. Bone china: 1974 in a limited edition of 100 2. Bronze metal: 1974 in a limited edition of 15
Series:	Racing Studies

Description	*Backstamp*	*U.S. $*	*Price* *Can. $*	*U.K. £*
1. Bone china	Black	4,375.00	5,625.00	2,500.00
2. Bronze metal	R-W	6,000.00	9,000.00	4,000.00

RW3951
HOBBY AND SWALLOW

Modeller:	James Alder
Height:	26 ½", 67.3 cm
Colour:	1. Greys and green 2. White
Plinth:	Wooden
Issued:	1. Coloured: 1974 in a limited edition of 250 2. White: 1974 in a limited edition of 100

Colourways	*Backstamp*	*U.S. $*	*Price* *Can. $*	*U.K. £*
1. Coloured (as above)	Black	1,500.00	2,000.00	1,000.00
2. White	Black	500.00	700.00	350.00

RW3952
CHELTENHAM

Modeller:	Bernard Winskill
Height:	Unknown
Colour:	1. Bone china: Rider One: Green, pink and white silks; black boots Rider Two: Lilac, grey and white silks; black boots Horses: Grey 2. Bronze metal
Plinth:	Wooden
Issued:	1. Bone china: 1978 in a limited edition of 100 2. Bronze metal: 1978 in a limited edition of 15
Series:	Racing Studies

Description	*Backstamp*	*U.S. $*	*Price* *Can. $*	*U.K. £*
1. Bone china	Black	4,375.00	5,625.00	2,500.00
2. Bronze metal	R-W	6,000.00	9,000.00	4,000.00

RW3955
RED RUM

Modeller: Doris Lindner
Height: 11", 27.9 cm
Colour: Chestnut
Plinth: Wooden
Issued: 1975 in a limited edition of 250
Series: Race Horses

Colourways	*Backstamp*	*U.S. $*	*Price Can. $*	*U.K. £*
Chestnut brown	Black	1,200.00	1,750.00	850.00

RW3956
ALEXANDER (The Great)

Modeller: Bernard Winskill
Height: 19", 48.3 cm
Colour: 1. Bone china: Fleshtone; white toga; brown horse
2. Bronze metal
Plinth: Wooden
Issued: 1. Bone china: 1975 in a limited edition of 250
2. Bronze metal: 1975 in a limited edition of 15
Series: Military Commanders

Description	*Backstamp*	*U.S. $*	*Price Can. $*	*U.K. £*
1. Bone china	Black	3,750.00	4,950.00	2,200.00
2. Bronze metal	R-W	6,000.00	8,000.00	3.500.00

RW3957
NEW BORN

Modeller: Doris Lindner
Height: 16", 40.6 cm
Colour: 1. Brown
2. White (Classic)
Plinth: Wooden
Issued: 1. Coloured: 1975 in a limited edition of 500
2. White: 1975 in a limited edition of 150

Colourways	*Backstamp*	*U.S. $*	*Price Can. $*	*U.K. £*
1. Coloured (as above)	Black	1,250.00	1,750.00	900.00
2. White	Black	425.00	600.00	300.00

RW3958
GALLOPING IN WINTER

Modeller: Doris Lindner
Height: 15 ¾", 40.0 cm
Colour: Grey
Plinth: Wooden, large oval
Issued: 1974 in a limited edition of 250
Varieties: Also called "Wild Horses" RW3466

			Price	
Colourways	*Backstamp*	*U.S. $*	*Can. $*	*U.K. £*
Grey	Black	1,500.00	1,850.00	900.00

RW3959A
AT THE START
Style One (No. 4)

Modeller: Bernard Winskill
Height: 21", 53.3 cm
Colour: 1. Bone china: Rider: Gold and black silks; white jodhpurs; black and gold boots; Horse: Brown
2. Bronze metal
Plinth: Wooden
Issued: 1. Bone china: 1975 in a limited edition of 100
2. Bronze metal: 1975 in a limited edition of 15
Series: Racing Studies

			Price	
Description	*Backstamp*	*U.S. $*	*Can. $*	*U.K. £*
1. Bone china	Black	1,300.00	1,675.00	750.00
2. Bronze metal	R-W	2,500.00	3,750.00	1,750.00

RW3959B
AT THE START
Style Two (No. 6)

Modeller: Bernard Winskill
Height: Unknown
Colour: Rider: Red silks; white jodhpurs; black boots
Horse: Brown
Issued: 1975 in a limited edition of 100
Series: Racing Studies

			Price	
Colourways	*Backstamp*	*U.S. $*	*Can. $*	*U.K. £*
Red/white/brown	Black	1,300.00	1,675.00	750.00

RW3960
DARTFORD WARBLER

Modeller:	James Alder
Height:	Unknown
Colour:	Brown, red and green
Plinth:	Wooden
Issued:	1975 in a limited edition of 500
Series:	British Birds, Series Two

			Price	
Colourways	*Backstamp*	*U.S. $*	*Can. $*	*U.K. £*
Brown/red/green	Black	550.00	800.00	400.00

RW3961
BEARDED REEDLING

Modeller:	James Alder
Height:	11", 27.9 cm
Colour:	Yellow and green
Plinth:	Wooden
Issued:	1975 in a limited edition of 500
Series:	British Birds, Series Two

			Price	
Colourways	*Backstamp*	*U.S. $*	*Can. $*	*U.K. £*
Yellow/green	Black	550.00	800.00	400.00

RW3962
SNOW BUNTING

Modeller:	James Alder
Height:	Unknown
Colour:	Grey, white and green
Plinth:	Wooden
Issued:	1975 in a limited edition of 500
Series:	British Birds, Series Two

			Price	
Colourways	*Backstamp*	*U.S. $*	*Can. $*	*U.K. £*
Grey/white	Black	550.00	800.00	400.00

RW3963
SHORELARK

Modeller: James Alder
Height: Unknown
Colour: Browns, black and white
Plinth: Wooden
Issued: 1975 in a limited edition of 500
Series: British Birds, Series Two

Colourways	*Backstamp*	*U.S. $*	*Price* *Can. $*	*U.K. £*
Browns	Black	550.00	800.00	400.00

RW3964
WALL CREEPER

Modeller: James Alder
Height: Unknown
Colour: Black, red and green
Plinth: Wooden
Issued: 1975 in a limited edition of 500
Series: British Birds, Series Two

Colourways	*Backstamp*	*U.S. $*	*Price* *Can. $*	*U.K. £*
Black/red/green	Black	550.00	800.00	400.00

RW3965
DIPPERS

Modeller: James Alder
Height: Unknown
Colour: Black, grey and green
Plinth: Wooden
Issued: 1976 in a limited edition of 500
Series: British Birds, Series Two

Colourways	*Backstamp*	*U.S. $*	*Price* *Can. $*	*U.K. £*
Black/grey/green	Black	550.00	800.00	400.00

RW3967
EXMOOR PONY

Modeller: Bernard Winskill
Height: 8 ¼", 21.0 cm
Colour: Brown and black
Plinth: Wooden
Issued: 1975 in a limited edition of 500

Colourways	*Backstamp*	*U.S. $*	*Price Can. $*	*U.K. £*
Brown/black	Black	750.00	1,100.00	500.00

RW3968
SHETLAND PONY

Modeller: Bernard Winskill
Height: 9", 22.9 cm
Colour: Light tan with cream tail and mane
Plinth: Wooden
Issued: 1976 in a limited edition of 500

Colourways	*Backstamp*	*U.S. $*	*Price Can. $*	*U.K. £*
Light tan/cream	Black	750.00	1,100.00	500.00

RW3981
KEK (KESTREL)

Modeller: James Alder
Height: 7 ½", 19.1 cm
Colour: 1. Bone china: Golden and dark brown, beige
2. Bronze metal
Issued: 1. Bone china: 1976
2. Bronze metal: 1975 in a limited edition of 50
Series: Hawks and Falcons

Description	*Backstamp*	*U.S. $*	*Price Can. $*	*U.K. £*
1. Bone china	Black	275.00	400.00	200.00
2. Bronze metal	R-W	425.00	600.00	300.00

RW3982
GRUNDY WITH PAT EDDERY UP

Modeller: Doris Lindner
Height: 11 ½", 29.2 cm
Colour: Jockey: Blue, white and yellow silks
Horse: Chestnut
Plinth: Wooden
Issued: 1976 in a limited edition of 500
Series: Racing Studies

			Price	
Colourways	*Backstamp*	*U.S. $*	*Can. $*	*U.K. £*
Blue/white/yellow/chestnut	Black	1,300.00	1,675.00	750.00

RW3989A
BORZOI
Style Two

Modeller: Kenneth Potts
Height: 5 ¼", 13.3 cm
Size: Small
Colour: 1. Bone china: Grey
2. Bronze metal
Issued: 1. Bone china: 1979-1984
2. Bronze metal: 1979 in a limited edition of 50

			Price	
Description	*Backstamp*	*U.S. $*	*Can. $*	*U.K. £*
1. Bone china	Black	300.00	400.00	175.00
2. Bronze metal	R-W		Rare	

RW3989B
SPRINGER SPANIEL

Modeller: Kenneth Potts
Height: 3 ¾", 9.5 cm
Size: Small
Colour: 1. Bone china: White with light brown patches
2. Bronze metal
Issued: 1. Bone china: 1979-1984
2. Bronze metal: 1979 in a limited edition of 50

			Price	
Description	*Backstamp*	*U.S. $*	*Can. $*	*U.K. £*
1. Bone china	Black	300.00	400.00	175.00
2. Bronze metal	R-W		Rare	

RW3992
ROUGH COLLIE WITH PUPS

Modeller: Kenneth Potts
Height: 5", 12.7 cm
Size: Small
Colour: 1. Bone china: Golden brown and cream
2. Bronze metal
Issued: 1. Coloured: 1978-1984
2. Bronze metal: 1977 in a limited edition of 50

Colourways	*Backstamp*	*U.S. $*	*Price Can. $*	*U.K. £*
1. Bone china	Black	300.00	400.00	175.00
2. Bronze metal	R-W		Rare	

RW3993
DICKCISSEL AND SUNFLOWER

Modeller: James Alder
Height: Unknown
Colour: Blue-grey, yellow and brown bird; yellow flowers; green stems and leaves; wooden plinth
Plinth: Wooden
Issued: 1977 in a limited edition of 150
Series: North American Birds

Colourways	*Backstamp*	*U.S. $*	*Price Can. $*	*U.K. £*
Blue-grey/yellow/black	Black	1,200.00	1,750.00	850.00

RW3994
CAROLINA WREN AND TRUMPET CREEPER

Modeller: James Alder
Height: Unknown
Colour: Orange and green; wooden plinth
Plinth: Wooden
Issued: 1976 in a limited edition of 150
Series: North American Birds

Colourways	*Backstamp*	*U.S. $*	*Price Can. $*	*U.K. £*
Orange/green	Black	1,350.00	1,900.00	950.00

RW3995
CHESTNUT-COLLARED LONGSPUR

Modeller: James Alder
Height: Unknown
Colour: Brown, grey, white, yellow and green
Plinth: Wooden
Issued: 1977 in a limited edition of 150
Series: North American Birds

Colourways	*Backstamp*	*U.S. $*	*Price Can. $*	*U.K. £*
Brown/grey/white	Black	1,100.00	1,500.00	800.00

RW3996
RUBY-CROWNED KINGLET AND CYPRESS

Modeller: James Alder
Height: Unknown
Colour: Green, yellow, cream and brown
Plinth: Wooden
Issued: 1976 in a limited edition of 150
Series: North American Birds

Colourways	*Backstamp*	*U.S. $*	*Price Can. $*	*U.K. £*
Green/yellow/cream	Black	600.00	800.00	450.00

RW3997
RED-BREASTED NUTHATCH AND OAK

Modeller: James Alder
Height: Unknown
Colour: Grey with red-yellow breast;
brown-green branch; green leaves
Plinth: Wooden
Issued: 1976 in a limited edition of 150
Series: North American Birds

Colourways	*Backstamp*	*U.S. $*	*Price Can. $*	*U.K. £*
Grey/red-yellow	Black	750.00	1,000.00	550.00

RW3998
RUFOUS HUMMINGBIRD

Modeller: James Alder
Height: Unknown
Colour: Orange bird; blue flowers; green leaves; wooden plinth
Plinth: Wooden
Issued: 1977 in a limited edition of 150
Series: North American Birds

Colourways	*Backstamp*	*U.S. $*	*Price Can. $*	*U.K. £*
Orange/blue/green	Black	1,350.00	1,900.00	950.00

RW3999
HIGHLAND BULL

Designer: Doris Lindner
Height: 8 ½", 21.4 cm
Colour: Brown
Plinth: Wooden
Issued: 1977 in a limited edition of 500

Colourways	*Backstamp*	*U.S. $*	*Price Can. $*	*U.K. £*
Brown	Black	1,200.00	1,500.00	750.00

RW4001
GREAT TIT FLEDGLING

Modeller: James Alder
Height: 3 ¾", 9.5 cm
Colour: Yellow, blue-grey and green
Issued: 1977-1980
Series: Fledglings

Colourways	*Backstamp*	*U.S. $*	*Price Can. $*	*U.K. £*
Yellow/blue-grey/green	Black	115.00	150.00	85.00

RW4002
WREN FLEDGLING ON LEAVES

Modeller: James Alder
Height: 3 ¾", 9.5 cm
Colour: Golden brown with white highlights; green leaves; grey base
Issued: 1977-1980
Series: Fledglings

Colourways	*Backstamp*	*U.S. $*	*Price Can. $*	*U.K. £*
Golden brown/white/green	Black	125.00	175.00	95.00

RW4003
ROBIN FLEDGLING ON BRANCH

Modeller: James Alder
Height: 4 ½", 11.9 cm
Colour: Browns, white and green
Issued: 1977-1980
Series: Fledglings

Colourways	*Backstamp*	*U.S. $*	*Price Can. $*	*U.K. £*
Browns/white/green	Black	125.00	175.00	95.00

RW4004
BLUE TIT FLEDGLING AND CLEMATIS

Modeller: James Alder
Height: 3 ¼", 8.3 cm
Colour: Yellow and grey bird; lilac flower; green leaves
Issued: 1977-1980
Series: Fledglings

Colourways	*Backstamp*	*U.S. $*	*Price Can. $*	*U.K. £*
Yellow/grey/lilac/green	Black	125.00	175.00	95.00

RW4005
BULLFINCH FLEDGLING ON APPLE BLOSSOM

Modeller: James Alder
Height: 3 ¼", 8.3 cm
Colour: Golden and dark brown and white bird; white and pink flowers; green leaves; brown branch
Issued: 1977-1980
Series: Fledglings

Colourways	*Backstamp*	*U.S. $*	*Price Can. $*	*U.K. £*
Golden brown/black/white	Black	115.00	150.00	85.00

RW4006
GOLDFINCH FLEDGLING AND THISTLE

Modeller: James Alder
Height: 3 ¼", 8.3 cm
Colour: Brown, yellow and black bird; mauve and green thistle
Issued: 1977-1980
Series: Fledglings

Colourways	*Backstamp*	*U.S. $*	*Price Can. $*	*U.K. £*
Brown/yellow/black	Black	115.00	150.00	85.00

RW4007
KITTEN (Seated)

Modeller: James Alder
Height: 4", 10.1 cm
Colour: Ginger with white
Issued: 1979-1983
Series: Kittens

Colourways	*Backstamp*	*U.S. $*	*Price Can. $*	*U.K. £*
Ginger/cream	Black	100.00	135.00	75.00

RW4008
LIPPIZANNER

Modeller: Bernard Winskill
Height: Unknown
Colour: Bronze metal
Plinth: Wooden
Issued: 1978 in a limited edition of 15

Description	*Backstamp*	*U.S. $*	*Price* *Can. $*	*U.K. £*
Bronze metal	R-W		Rare	

Note: Not produced in bone china.

RW4009
SPARROWHAWK

Modeller: James Alder
Height: 7 ½", 19.1 cm
Colour: 1. Bone china: Coloured
2. Bronze metal
Plinth: Wooden
Issued: 1. Bone china: 1978 in a limited edition of 250
2. Bronze metal: 1978 in a limited edition of 50
Series: Hawks and Falcons

Description	*Backstamp*	*U.S. $*	*Price* *Can. $*	*U.K. £*
1. Bone china	Black	275.00	400.00	200.00
2. Bronze metal	R-W	425.00	600.00	300.00

Photograph not available at press time

RW4010
RED SETTER (Lying on base)

Modeller: Kenneth Potts
Height: 6 ¼", 15.9 cm
Colour: 1. Bone china: Red-brown
2. Bronze metal
Plinth: Wooden
Issued: 1. Bone china: 1979 in a limited edition of 250
2. Bronze metal: 1979 in a limited edition of 25

Description	*Backstamp*	*U.S. $*	*Price* *Can. $*	*U.K. £*
1. Bone china	Black	450.00	600.00	325.00
2. Bronze metal	R-W		Rare	

RW4015
MISTRAL AND LESTER PIGGOT

Modeller: Bernard Winskill
Height: 16", 40.6 cm
Colour: 1. Bone china: Rider: Blue, green and white silks; white jodhpurs
Horse: Chestnut
2. Bronze metal
Plinth: Wooden
Issued: 1. Bone china: 1978 in a limited edition of 150
2. Bronze metal: 1978 in a limited edition of 25
Series: Racing Studies

Description	*Backstamp*	*U.S. $*	*Price Can. $*	*U.K. £*
1. Bone china	Black	2,650.00	3,375.00	1,500.00
2. Bronze metal	R-W	4,275.00	5,600.00	2,500.00

RW4016
WELSH COB STALLION "LLANARTH FLYING COMET"

Modeller: Lorne McKean
Height: 11", 27.9 cm
Colour: 1. Bone china: Black
2. Bronze metal
Plinth: Wooden
Issued: 1. Bone china: 1978 in a limited edition of 250
2. Bronze metal: 1978 in a limited edition of 15

Description	*Backstamp*	*U.S. $*	*Price Can. $*	*U.K. £*
1. Bone china	Black	850.00	1,250.00	550.00
2. Bronze metal	R-W		Rare	

RW4017
DUNFERMLINE

Modeller: Bernard Winskill
Height: 11", 27.9 cm
Colour: Bronze metal
Issued: 1978 in a limited edition of 25

Description	*Backstamp*	*U.S. $*	*Price Can. $*	*U.K. £*
Bronze metal	R-W		Rare	

Photograph not available at press time

RW4018
ROBIN ON CHRISTMAS ROSE

Modeller:	James Alder
Height:	7 ¾", 19.7 cm
Colour:	Red breast; grey and brown feathers; white rose; green leaves
Issued:	1978 in a limited edition of 250
Series:	British Birds, Series Two

Colourways	*Backstamp*	*U.S. $*	*Price Can. $*	*U.K. £*
Brown/red/white	Black	350.00	475.00	250.00

RW4019
WOODWARBLER ON CHERRY

Modeller:	James Alder
Height:	7 ¾", 18.5 cm
Colour:	Green and brown bird; white flowers; brown branch; green leaves
Issued:	1978 in a limited edition of 250
Series:	British Birds, Series Two

Colourways	*Backstamp*	*U.S. $*	*Price Can. $*	*U.K. £*
Green/brown/white	Black	350.00	475.00	250.00

RW4020
KITTEN (Lying)
Style One

Modeller:	James Alder
Length:	5 ¼", 13.5 cm
Colour:	Black and white
Issued:	1979-1983
Series:	Kittens

Colourways	*Backstamp*	*U.S. $*	*Price Can. $*	*U.K. £*
Black/white	Black	100.00	135.00	75.00

RW4027
PERSIAN KITTEN (Seated)

Modeller: James Alder
Height: 4", 10.1 cm
Colour: 1. Blue
2. Cream
Issued: 1978-1985
Series: Kittens

Colourways	*Backstamp*	*U.S. $*	*Price Can. $*	*U.K. £*
Coloured (as above)	Black	100.00	135.00	75.00

RW4028
OLD ENGLISH SHEEPDOG (Seated)

Modeller: Kenneth Potts
Height: 5", 12.5 cm
Size: Small
Colour: 1. Bone china: Grey and white
2. Bronze metal
Issued: 1. Bone china: 1978
2. Bronze metal: 1978 in a limited edition of 25

Description	*Backstamp*	*U.S. $*	*Price Can. $*	*U.K. £*
1. Bone china	Black	275.00	400.00	200.00
2. Bronze metal	R-W	425.00	600.00	300.00

RW4029
BLUE TIT ON HOGWEED

Modeller: James Alder
Height: 8", 20.3 cm
Colour: Green and yellow
Issued: 1978 in a limited edition of 250
Series: British Birds, Series Two

Colourways	*Backstamp*	*U.S. $*	*Price Can. $*	*U.K. £*
Green/yellow	Black	350.00	475.00	250.00

RW4030
LITTLE OWL ON IVY

Modeller: James Alder
Height: 7 ¼", 18.4 cm
Colour: 1. Bone china: Brown, cream, yellow and green
2. Bronze metal
Issued: 1. Bone china: 1978 in a limited edition of 250
2. Bronze metal: 1978 in a limited edition of 25
Series: British Birds, Series Two

Description	Backstamp	U.S. $	Price Can. $	U.K. £
1. Bone china	Black	350.00	450.00	250.00
2. Bronze metal	R-W		Rare	

RW4031
H.R.H. PRINCE CHARLES ON PANS FOLLY

Modeller: Lorne McKean
Height: 16", 40.6 cm
Colour: 1. Bone china: Green shirt; white jodhpurs; brown boots; black hat; brown horse
2. Bronze metal
Plinth: Wooden
Issued: 1. Bone china: 1978 in a limited edition of 250
2. Bronze metal: 1978 in a limited edition of 15

Description	Backstamp	U.S. $	Price Can. $	U.K. £
1. Bone china	Black	1,650.00	2,125.00	950.00
2. Bronze metal	R-W	3,500.00	4,500.00	2,000.00

RW4034
RICHARD COEUR DE LION

Modeller: Bernard Winskill
Height: 15 ½", 39.4 cm
Colour: 1. Bone china: Red cape and reins; grey tunic and horse
2. Bronze metal
Plinth: Wooden
Issued: 1. Bone china: 1978 in a limited edition of 250
2. Bronze metal: 1978 in a limited edition of 15
Series: Military Commanders

Description	Backstamp	U.S. $	Price Can. $	U.K. £
1. Bone china	Black	4,375.00	5,600.00	2,500.00
2. Bronze metal	R-W	6,000.00	9,000.00	4,000.00

RW4035
BOXER (Seated)

Modeller: Kenneth Potts
Height: 9 ½", 24.0 cm
Size: Large
Colour: 1. Bone china: Tan with black facial markings
2. Bronze metal
Issued: 1. Bone china: 1978 in a limited edition of 250
2. Bronze metal: 1978 in a limited edition of 25

Description	*Backstamp*	*U.S. $*	*Price Can. $*	*U.K. £*
1. Bone china	Black	375.00	550.00	275.00
2. Bronze metal	R-W		Rare	

RW4036
LABRADOR (Seated)

Modeller: Kenneth Potts
Height: 10 ¼", 26.0 cm
Size: Large
Colour: 1. Bone china: Golden
2. Bronze metal
Issued: 1. Bone china: 1978 in a limited edition of 250
2. Bronze metal: 1978 in a limited edition of 25

Description	*Backstamp*	*U.S. $*	*Price Can. $*	*U.K. £*
1. Bone china	Black	375.00	550.00	275.00
2. Bronze metal	R-W		Rare	

RW4037
CONNEMARA

Modeller: Lorne McKean
Height: 13 ½", 34.3 cm
Colour: 1. Bone china: Grey
2. Bronze metal
Issued: 1. Bone china: 1978 in a limited edition of 250
2. Bronze metal: 1978 in a limited edition

Description	*Backstamp*	*U.S. $*	*Price Can. $*	*U.K. £*
1. Bone china	Black	950.00	1,350.00	650.00
2. Bronze metal	R-W		Rare	

RW4040
YELLOW BUNTING ON BLACKBERRY

Modeller: James Alder
Height: 6″, 15.0 cm
Colour: Yellow, green and orange bird; purple berries; white flowers; green leaves
Issued: 1978 in a limited edition of 250
Series: British Birds, Series Two

Colourways	*Backstamp*	*U.S. $*	*Price Can. $*	*U.K. £*
Yellow/green/orange	Black	350.00	450.00	250.00

RW4043
AFGHAN HOUND

Modeller: Kenneth Potts
Height: 5 ¾″, 14.6 cm
Size: Small
Colour: Golden brown
Issued: 1978

Colourways	*Backstamp*	*U.S. $*	*Price Can. $*	*U.K. £*
Golden brown	Black	225.00	300.00	150.00

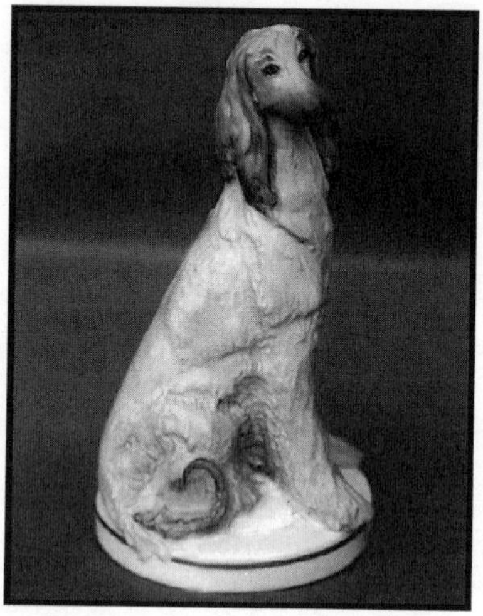

RW4045
PERSIAN KITTEN (On hind legs)

Modeller: James Alder
Height: 4″, 10.1 cm
Colour: White kitten; blue bow
Issued: 1979-1985
Series: Kittens

Colourways	*Backstamp*	*U.S. $*	*Price Can. $*	*U.K. £*
White/blue	Black	100.00	135.00	75.00

RW4046
SIAMESE KITTEN

Modeller: James Alder
Height: 4", 10.1 cm
Colour: Sealpoint with grey markings; blue eyes
Issued: 1979-1985
Series: Kittens

Colourways	*Backstamp*	*U.S. $*	*Price Can. $*	*U.K. £*
Sealpoint	Black	100.00	135.00	75.00

RW4047
TABBY KITTEN (Lying)

Modeller: James Alder
Height: 4", 10.1 cm
Colour: Dark and light brown with white markings
Issued: 1979-1985
Series: Kittens

Colourways	*Backstamp*	*U.S. $*	*Price Can. $*	*U.K. £*
Brown/white	Black	100.00	135.00	75.00

RW4048
LINNET ON WILD ROSE

Modeller: James Alder
Height: 7", 17.8 cm
Colour: Brown, cream and red bird; pink flower; green leaves
Issued: 1980 in a limited edition of 250
Series: British Birds, Series Two

Colourways	*Backstamp*	*U.S. $*	*Price Can. $*	*U.K. £*
Brown/cream/pink/green	Black	350.00	450.00	250.00

RW4055
EUGÉNE DE BEAUHARNAIS / CHASSEUR AND CHAVAL

Modeller:	Bernard Winskill
Height:	Unknown
Colour:	1. Red and black jacket; cream jodhpurs; black saddle pad; brown horse 2. Red and yellow jacket; white jodhpurs; cream and gold saddle pad; light brown horse
Plinth:	Wooden
Issued:	1980 in a limited edition of 250
Series:	Military Commanders

Colourways	*Backstamp*	*U.S. $*	*Price Can. $*	*U.K. £*
Coloured (as above)	Black	4,375.00	5,600.00	2,000.00

RW4056
MARSH TIT ON DAPHNE

Modeller:	James Alder
Height:	7 ¾", 19.7 cm
Colour:	Brown, black and white bird; pink flowers; brown stalk
Issued:	1979 in a limited edition of 250
Series:	British Birds, Series Two

Colourways	*Backstamp*	*U.S. $*	*Price Can. $*	*U.K. £*
Unknown	Black	350.00	450.00	250.00

RW4057
GREENFINCH ON FORSYTHIA

Modeller:	James Alder
Height:	Unknown
Colour:	Yellow and green
Issued:	1979 in a limited edition of 250
Series:	British Birds, Series Two

Colourways	*Backstamp*	*U.S. $*	*Price Can. $*	*U.K. £*
Yellow/green	Black	350.00	450.00	250.00

RW4061
GREENFINCH ON BEECH

Modeller:	James Alder
Height:	4", 10.1 cm
Size:	Small
Colour:	Green, black and brown
Issued:	1979
Series:	British Birds, Series Three

Colourways	*Backstamp*	*U.S. $*	*Price Can. $*	*U.K. £*
Green/black/brown	Black	100.00	135.00	75.00

RW4067
WILLIAM THE CONQUEROR

Modeller:	Bernard Winskill
Height:	17", 43.2 cm
Colour:	1. Bone china: Dark brown, tan and blue 2. Bronze metal
Plinth:	Wooden
Issued:	1. Bone china: 1980 in a limited edition of 250 2. Bronze metal: 1980 in a limited edition of 15
Series:	Military Commanders

Description	*Backstamp*	*U.S. $*	*Price Can. $*	*U.K. £*
1. Bone china	Black	4,375.00	5,600.00	2,500.00
2. Bronze metal	R-W	6,000.00	9,000.00	4,000.00

RW4068
REDSTART

Modeller:	James Alder
Height:	4 ½", 11.9 cm
Size:	Small
Colour:	Grey, red and black
Issued:	1979
Series:	British Birds, Series Three

Colourways	*Backstamp*	*U.S. $*	*Price Can. $*	*U.K. £*
Grey/red/black	Black	100.00	135.00	75.00

RW4070
GREY WAGTAIL

Modeller:	James Alder
Height:	3 ½", 8.9 cm
Size:	Small
Colour:	Grey and yellow
Issued:	1979
Series:	British Birds, Series Three

Colourways	*Backstamp*	*U.S. $*	*Price* *Can. $*	*U.K. £*
Grey/yellow	Black	100.00	135.00	75.00

RW4071
ROBIN ON HOLLY
Style One

Modeller:	James Alder
Height:	4", 10.1 cm
Size:	Small
Colour:	Brown and red bird; yellow berries; green leaves
Issued:	1979
Series:	British Birds, Series Three

Colourways	*Backstamp*	*U.S. $*	*Price* *Can. $*	*U.K. £*
Yellow/brown	Black	100.00	135.00	75.00

RW4076
SIMÓN BOLÍVAR

Modeller:	Bernard Winskill
Height:	15 ½", 39.4 cm
Colour:	Rider: Navy jacket with golf epaulettes; white jodhpurs Horse: Grey
Plinth:	Wooden
Issued:	1979 in a limited edition of 250
Series:	Military Commanders

Colourways	*Backstamp*	*U.S. $*	*Price* *Can. $*	*U.K. £*
Navy/white/grey	Black	3,500.00	4,500.00	2,000.00

RW4077
STONECHAT

Modeller:	James Alder
Height:	4", 10.1 cm
Size:	Small
Colour:	Yellow breast; black head and wings; yellow flower; green-brown base
Issued:	1979
Series:	British Birds, Series Three

			Price	
Colourways	*Backstamp*	*U.S. $*	*Can. $*	*U.K. £*
Yellow/black	Black	100.00	135.00	75.00

RW4078
CRESTED TIT

Modeller:	James Alder
Height:	3 ¾", 9.5 cm
Size:	Small
Colour:	Pale brown, cream, black and white
Issued:	1979
Series:	British Birds, Series Three

			Price	
Colourways	*Backstamp*	*U.S. $*	*Can. $*	*U.K. £*
Pale brown/cream/black/white	Black	100.00	135.00	75.00

RW4081
OLD ENGLISH SHEEPDOG PUPPY (Playing)

Modeller:	Kenneth Potts
Height:	10", 25.4 cm
Size:	Large
Colour:	Grey and white
Issued:	1979 in a limited edition of 250

			Price	
Colourways	*Backstamp*	*U.S. $*	*Can. $*	*U.K. £*
Grey/white	Black	400.00	550.00	275.00

RW4093
BOXER (Standing)

Modeller:	Doris Lindner
Height:	10 ¼", 26.0 cm
Size:	Large
Colour:	Brown and white
Plinth:	Wooden
Issued:	1981 in a limited edition of 1,000
Series:	Final Collection by Doris Lindner

			Price	
Colourways	***Backstamp***	***U.S. $***	***Can. $***	***U.K. £***
Brown/white	Black	700.00	1,000.00	500.00

RW4094
THE SALUKI

Modeller:	Doris Lindner
Height:	9 ¼", 23.5 cm
Size:	Large
Colour:	White with grey and tan
Plinth:	Wooden
Issued:	1981 in a limited edition of 1,000
Series:	Final Collection by Doris Lindner

			Price	
Colourways	***Backstamp***	***U.S. $***	***Can. $***	***U.K. £***
White/grey/tan	Black	750.00	1,000.00	500.00

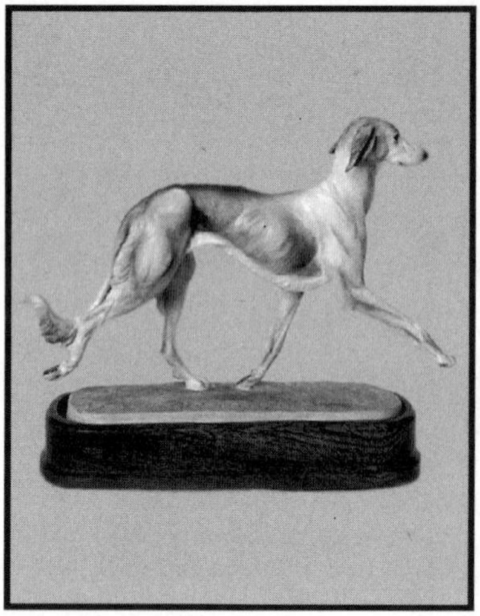

RW4095
PONY STALLION

Modeller:	Doris Lindner
Height:	Unknown
Colour:	Brown
Plinth:	Wooden
Issued:	1981 in a limited edition of 500
Series:	Final Collection by Doris Lindner

			Price	
Colourways	***Backstamp***	***U.S. $***	***Can. $***	***U.K. £***
Brown	Black	950.00	1,350.00	600.00

RW4096
HUNTER

Modeller: Doris Lindner
Height: 11 ½", 29.2 cm
Colour: Grey
Plinth: Wooden
Issued: 1981 in a limited edition of 1,000
Series: Final Collection by Doris Lindner

Colourways	*Backstamp*	*U.S. $*	*Price Can. $*	*U.K. £*
Grey	Black	950.00	1,350.00	600.00

RW4101
WREN ON CLEMATIS

Modeller: James Alder
Height: 7 ¼", 18.4 cm
Colour: Brown bird; pink and yellow flower; bronze stem and leaves
Issued: 1981
Series: Nature Studies

Colourways	*Backstamp*	*U.S. $*	*Price Can. $*	*U.K. £*
Brown/pink/yellow/bronze	R-W	200.00	300.00	150.00

RW4102
NIGHTINGALE ON HONEYSUCKLE
Style Two

Modeller: James Alder
Height: 10", 25.4 cm
Colour: Brown and cream bird; pink and yellow flowers; bronze stem and leaves
Issued: 1981
Series: Nature Studies

Colourways	*Backstamp*	*U.S. $*	*Price Can. $*	*U.K. £*
Brown/cream/pink/bronze	R-W	200.00	300.00	150.00

RW4103
ROBIN ON HOLLY
Style Two

Modeller: James Alder
Height: 7 ¼", 18.4 cm
Colour: Brown and red bird; red berrries; bronze stem and leaves
Issued: 1981
Series: Nature Studies

Colourways	*Backstamp*	*U.S. $*	*Price Can. $*	*U.K. £*
Brown/red/white/bronze	R-W	200.00	300.00	150.00

RW4106
THOROUGHBRED FOAL

Modeller: Doris Lindner
Height: 6", 15.0 cm
Colour: Brown and cream
Plinth: Wooden
Issued: 1981 in a limited edition of 1,000
Series: Final Collection by Doris Lindner

Colourways	*Backstamp*	*U.S. $*	*Price Can. $*	*U.K. £*
Brown/cream	Black	750.00	1,150.00	500.00

RW4107
THOROUGHBRED MARE

Modeller: Doris Lindner
Height: 10 ¼", 26.0 cm
Colour: Palomino
Plinth: Wooden
Issued: 1981 in a limited edition of 1,000
Series: Final Collection by Doris Lindner

Colourways	*Backstamp*	*U.S. $*	*Price Can. $*	*U.K. £*
Palomino	Black	950.00	1,350.00	650.00

RW4108
WATERLILY AND BUTTERFLY

Modeller: James Alder
Height: 9 ½", 24.0 cm
Colour: Crimson flower; white butterfly; bronze stem and leaves
Issued: 1981
Series: Nature Studies

Colourways	Backstamp	U.S. $	Price Can. $	U.K. £
Crimson/white/bronze	R-W	200.00	300.00	150.00

Photograph not available at press time

RW4111
HEDGEHOG ON BRONZE
Style One

Modeller: James Alder
Height: 4", 10.1 cm
Colour: Brown
Issued: 1980
Series: Nature Studies

Colourways	Backstamp	U.S. $	Price Can. $	U.K. £
Brown	R-W	100.00	135.00	75.00

RW4116
GOLDCREST ON BRONZE
Style One

Modeller: James Alder
Height: Unknown
Colour: Greenish-yellow and brown bird; bronze branch
Issued: 1981
Series: Nature Studies

Colourways	Backstamp	U.S. $	Price Can. $	U.K. £
Greenish-yellow/brown/bronze	R-W	100.00	135.00	75.00

RW4117
BLUE TIT ON BRONZE
Style One

Modeller: James Alder
Height: 7", 17.8 cm
Colour: Yellow, blue and black bird; bronze branch and leaves
Issued: 1981
Series: Nature Studies

Colourways	*Backstamp*	*Price U.S. $*	*Can. $*	*U.K. £*
Yellow/blue/black/bronze	R-W	100.00	135.00	75.00

RW4118
BULLFINCH ON BRONZE

Modeller: James Alder
Height: 5 ½", 14.0 cm
Colour: Grey, black and red bird; white flowers; bronze branch and leaves
Issued: 1981
Series: Nature Studies

Colourways	*Backstamp*	*Price U.S. $*	*Can. $*	*U.K. £*
Grey/black/red/bronze	R-W	100.00	135.00	75.00

RW4144
FRENCH BULLDOG "WINSTON"

Modeller: James Alder
Height: 3", 7.6 cm
Colour: Black with white patch on chest
Issued: Unknown

Colourways	*Backstamp*	*Price U.S. $*	*Can. $*	*U.K. £*
Black	Black		Rare	

Note: Approximately 15 models were made. The dog 'Winston' belonged to Lynn Davies, Managing Director of Royal Worcester 1977-1979 and Chief Executive 1979-1984.

RW4162
ARAB STALLION

Modeller: Donald Brindley
Height: Unknown
Colour: Unknown
Plinth: Wooden
Issued: 1982 in a limited edition of 500

Colourways	*Backstamp*	*U.S. $*	*Price Can. $*	*U.K. £*
Grey	Black	1,000.00	1,500.00	750.00

Photograph not available at press time

Note: Commissioned by L'Atelier Art Editions.

RW4172
POINTER SLEEPING

Modeller: Kenneth Potts
Height: 1 ¼", 3.1 cm
Colour: White and gold
Issued: 1985-1991
Series: Country Life Cameos

Colourways	*Backstamp*	*U.S. $*	*Price Can. $*	*U.K. £*
White/gold	Black	60.00	75.00	40.00

RW4173
FOXHOUND (Standing)
Style Three

Modeller: Kenneth Potts
Height: 1 ¼", 3.1 cm
Colour: 1. White and gold
2. White and tan
Issued: 1985-1991
Series: Country Life Cameos

Colourways	*Backstamp*	*U.S. $*	*Price Can. $*	*U.K. £*
1. White/gold	Black	60.00	75.00	40.00
2. White/tan	Black	75.00	100.00	60.00

RW4174
SALMON
Style Three

Modeller: Kenneth Potts
Height: 1 ¼", 3.1 cm
Colour: 1. Creamy-yellow with red spots and gilt highlights
2. White and gold
Issued: 1985-1991
Series: Country Life Cameos

			Price	
Colourways	*Backstamp*	*U.S. $*	*Can. $*	*U.K. £*
1. Creamy-yellow/red/gilt	Black	75.00	100.00	60.00
2. White/gold	Black	60.00	75.00	40.00

RW4175
FOX
Style Two

Modeller: Kenneth Potts
Height: 1 ¼", 3.1 cm
Colour: 1. Grey with gilt highlights
2. White and gold
Issued: 1985-1991
Series: Country Life Cameos

			Price	
Colourways	*Backstamp*	*U.S. $*	*Can. $*	*U.K. £*
1. Grey/gilt	Black	75.00	100.00	60.00
2. White/gold	Black	60.00	75.00	40.00

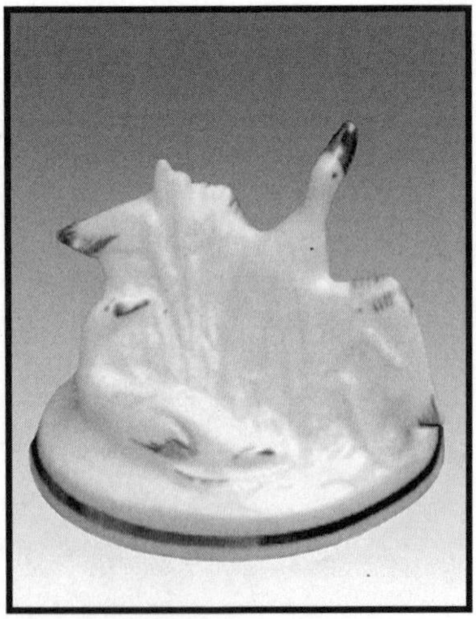

RW4176
MALLARDS

Modeller: Kenneth Potts
Height: 1 ¾", 4.5 cm
Colour: White and gold
Issued: 1985-1991
Series: Country Life Cameos

			Price	
Colourways	*Backstamp*	*U.S. $*	*Can. $*	*U.K. £*
White/gold	Black	60.00	75.00	40.00

RW4177
OTTER

Modeller: Kenneth Potts
Height: 1", 2.5 cm
Colour: 1. White and gilt; blue base
2. White; gold line around base
Issued: 1985-1991
Series: Country Life Cameos

Colourways	*Backstamp*	*U.S. $*	*Price Can. $*	*U.K. £*
1. White/gilt/blue	Black	75.00	100.00	60.00
2. White/gold	Black	60.00	75.00	40.00

Photograph not available at press time

RW4178
CAROLINA WREN AND WILD ROSE

Modeller: David Fryer
Height: 4 ½", 11.9 cm
Colour: Unknown
Issued: 1985
Series: American Birds on Bronze (Small size)

Colourways	*Backstamp*	*U.S. $*	*Price Can. $*	*U.K. £*
Unknown	R-W	100.00	135.00	75.00

RW4179
ROBIN AND NARCISSUS

Modeller: David Fryer
Height: 6 ¾", 17.2 cm
Colour: Red and brown bird; lemon-yellow flowers; bronze leaves and base
Issued: 1985
Series: American Birds on Bronze (Small size)

Colourways	*Backstamp*	*U.S. $*	*Price Can. $*	*U.K. £*
Red/brown/lemon/bronze	R-W	100.00	135.00	75.00

RW4180
RED CARDINAL ON BRONZE

Modeller: David Fryer
Height: 4", 10.1 cm
Colour: Red bird; pink flowers; bronze stems, leaves and base
Issued: 1985
Series: American Birds on Bronze (Small size)

Colourways	Backstamp	Price U.S. $	Can. $	U.K. £
Red/white/bronze	R-W	100.00	135.00	75.00

RW4181
CHICKADEE AND DAISIES

Modeller: David Fryer
Height: 5 ½", 14.0 cm
Colour: Brown, white and black bird; white flowers; bronze stem, leaves and base
Issued: 1985
Series: American Birds on Bronze (Small size)

Colourways	Backstamp	Price U.S. $	Can. $	U.K. £
Brown/white/black/bronze	R-W	100.00	135.00	75.00

RW4186
BLUEBIRD AND PINE CONES

Modeller: David Fryer
Height: 5", 12.7 cm
Colour: Blue and orange bird; brown pine cones; bronze foliage and base
Issued: 1985
Series: American Birds on Bronze (Small size)

Colourways	Backstamp	Price U.S. $	Can. $	U.K. £
Blue/orange/brown/bronze	R-W	100.00	135.00	75.00

RW4196
STAG BEETLE

Modeller: Kenneth Potts
Height: 1", 2.5 cm
Colour: Unknown
Issued: 1983
Series: Country Life Cameos

Colourways	*Backstamp*	*U.S. $*	*Price* *Can. $*	*U.K. £*
Unknown	Black	75.00	100.00	60.00

Photograph not available at press time

RW4197
SNAIL
Style Two

Modeller: Kenneth Potts
Height: ¾", 1.9 cm
Colour: 1. Pale blue and gold
2. White and gold
Issued: 1989-1991
Series: Country Life Cameos

Colourways	*Backstamp*	*U.S. $*	*Price* *Can. $*	*U.K. £*
1. Pale blue/gold	Black	75.00	100.00	60.00
2. White/gold	Black	60.00	75.00	40.00

RW4198
FROG

Modeller: Kenneth Potts
Height: 1 ¼", 3.1 cm
Colour: Creamy-yellow with gold spots
Issued: 1989-1991
Series: Country Life Cameos

Colourways	*Backstamp*	*U.S. $*	*Price* *Can. $*	*U.K. £*
Creamy-yellow/gold	Black	75.00	100.00	60.00

RW4209
HARVEST MOUSE ON BRONZE

Modeller:	David Fryer
Height:	5 ½", 14.0 cm
Colour:	Grey mouse; white flowers; bronze foliage and base
Issued:	1984-1986
Series:	Woodland Animals on Bronze

			Price	
Colourways	*Backstamp*	*U.S. $*	*Can. $*	*U.K. £*
Grey/white/bronze	R-W	115.00	150.00	85.00

RW4210
BARN OWL (TYTO ALBA)

Modeller:	David Fryer
Height:	25", 63.5 cm
Colour:	Bone china bird and ivy; bronze and glass window
Plinth:	Wooden
Issued:	1984 in a limited edition of 100
Series:	Ornamental Studio (Large size)

			Price	
Colourways	*Backstamp*	*U.S. $*	*Can. $*	*U.K. £*
Brown/ivory/bronze	Black	2,750.00	3,500.00	1,750.00

Note: A variation of RW4210 was commissioned with white flowers around the lower corner of the window frame. Few models were made.

RW4211
HARE ON BRONZE

Modeller:	David Fryer
Height:	4 ¾", 12.1 cm
Colour:	Brown and white hare; red flowers; bronze foliage and base
Issued:	1984-1986
Series:	Woodland Animals on Bronze (Small size)

			Price	
Colourways	*Backstamp*	*U.S. $*	*Can. $*	*U.K. £*
Brown/white/red/bronze	R-W	115.00	150.00	85.00

RW4212
HEDGEHOG ON BRONZE
Style Two

Modeller: David Fryer
Height: 4 ¼", 10.8 cm
Colour: Brown hedgehog; mauve flower; bronze foliage and base
Issued: 1984-1986
Series: Woodland Animals on Bronze

Colourways	*Backstamp*	*U.S. $*	*Price* *Can. $*	*U.K. £*
Brown/mauve/bronze	R-W	115.00	150.00	85.00

Photograph not available at press time

RW4214
BELTED KINGFISHER AND WATER LILY

Modeller: David Fryer
Height: 7", 17.8 cm
Colour: Blue and orange bird; yellow flower; bronze foliage and base
Issued: 1985

Colourways	*Backstamp*	*U.S. $*	*Price* *Can. $*	*U.K. £*
Blue/orange/yellow/bronze	R-W	100.00	135.00	75.00

RW4219
FOX ON BRONZE

Modeller: David Fryer
Height: 3 ½", 8.9 cm
Colour: Red-brown and white fox; lemon-yellow narcissus; bronze foliage and base
Issued: 1984-1986
Series: Woodland Animals on Bronze

Colourways	*Backstamp*	*U.S. $*	*Price* *Can. $*	*U.K. £*
Red-brown/lemon-yellow/bronze	R-W	115.00	150.00	85.00

RW4237
DORMOUSE ON BRONZE

Modeller: David Fryer
Height: 5 ½", 14.0 cm
Colour: Brown mouse; pink flowers; bronze foliage and base
Issued: 1984-1986
Series: Woodland Animals on Bronze

Colourways	*Backstamp*	*U.S. $*	*Price Can. $*	*U.K. £*
Brown/pink/bronze	R-W	115.00	150.00	85.00

RW4238
RED SQUIRREL ON BRONZE

Modeller: David Fryer
Height: 5 ½", 14.0 cm
Colour: Red-brown and white squirrel; yellow flowers; bronze foliage and base
Issued: 1984-1986
Series: Woodland Animals on Bronze

Colourways	*Backstamp*	*U.S. $*	*Price Can. $*	*U.K. £*
Red-brown/white/yellow/bronze	R-W	115.00	150.00	85.00

Photograph not available at press time

RW4240
KESTREL (Domed)

Modeller: David Fryer
Height: 7", 17.8 cm
Colour: Golden and dark brown and white bird; pink flowers; bronze foliage and base
Issued: 1984-1987
Series: Birds of Prey on Bronze (Small size)

Colourways	*Backstamp*	*U.S. $*	*Price Can. $*	*U.K. £*
Golden/brown/pink/bronze	R-W	200.00	275.00	150.00

Note: Issued with a wooden plinth and a glass dome (8" x 4").

RW4241
BARN OWL (Domed)

Modeller: David Fryer
Height: 7", 17.8 cm
Colour: Golden brown and cream bird; pink flowers; bronze foliage and base
Issued: 1984-1987
Series: Birds of Prey on Bronze (Small size)

Colourways	*Backstamp*	*Price* *U.S. $*	*Can. $*	*U.K. £*
Golden/cream/bronze	R-W	200.00	275.00	150.00

Note: Issued with a wooden plinth and a glass dome (8" x 4").

RW4243
PEREGRINE FALCON (Domed)
Style Two

Modeller: David Fryer
Height: 7", 17.8 cm
Colour: Brown and white bird; bronze foliage and base
Issued: 1985
Series: Birds of Prey on Bronze (Small size)

Colourways	*Backstamp*	*Price* *U.S. $*	*Can. $*	*U.K. £*
Brown/white/bronze	R-W	200.00	275.00	150.00

Note: Issued with a wooden plinth and a glass dome (8" x 4").

RW4246
MARSH HARRIER (Domed)

Modeller: David Fryer
Height: 7", 17.8 cm
Colour: Grey and white bird; white flowers; bronze foliage and base
Issued: 1984-1987
Series: Birds of Prey on Bronze (Small size)

Colourways	*Backstamp*	*Price* *U.S. $*	*Can. $*	*U.K. £*
Grey/white/bronze	R-W	200.00	275.00	150.00

Photograph not available at press time

Note: Issued with a wooden plinth and a glass dome (8" x 4").

Photograph not available at press time

RW4260
SHORT-EARED OWL (Domed)

Modeller: David Fryer
Height: 7", 17.8 cm
Colour: Golden and dark brown; white flowers; bronze foliage and base
Issued: 1984-1987
Series: Birds of Prey on Bronze (Small size)

Colourways	*Backstamp*	*U.S. $*	*Price Can. $*	*U.K. £*
Golden/brown/white/bronze	R-W	200.00	275.00	150.00

Note: Issued with a wooden plinth and a glass dome (8" x 4").

RW4264
BUMBLEBEE

Modeller: Kenneth Potts
Height: 1 ¼", 3.1 cm
Colour: Yellow, black and white with gilt highlights
Issued: 1989-1991
Series: Country Life Cameos

Colourways	*Backstamp*	*U.S. $*	*Price Can. $*	*U.K. £*
Yellow/black/white	Black	75.00	100.00	60.00

RW4265
GRASSHOPPER

Modeller: Kenneth Potts
Height: 1 ¼", 3.1 cm
Colour: Green, yellow and salmon; gilt highlights
Issued: 1989-1991
Series: Country Life Cameos

Colourways	*Backstamp*	*U.S. $*	*Price Can. $*	*U.K. £*
Green/yellow/salmon	Black	75.00	100.00	60.00

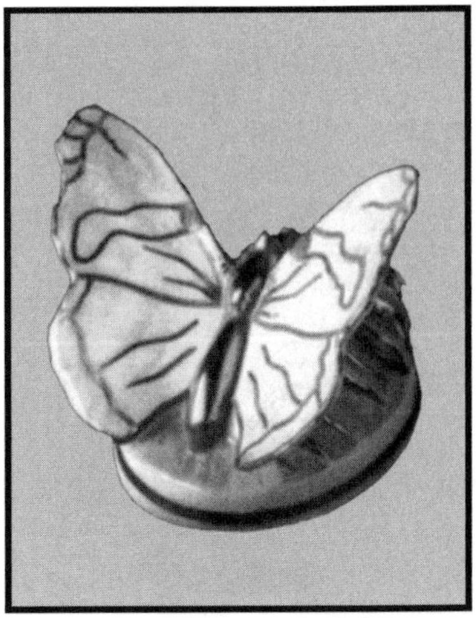

RW4267
BUTTERFLY

Modeller: Kenneth Potts
Height: 1 ¼″, 3.1 cm
Colour: Cream with gilt highlights
Issued: 1989-1991
Series: Country Life Cameos

Colourways	*Backstamp*	*U.S. $*	*Price Can. $*	*U.K. £*
Cream/gilt	Black	75.00	100.00	60.00

Photograph not available at press time

RW4270
BALD EAGLE (Domed)

Modeller: David Fryer
Height: 7″, 17.8 cm
Colour: Brown and white bird; orange flowers; bronze foliage and base
Issued: 1984-1987
Series: Birds of Prey on Bronze (Small size)

Colourways	*Backstamp*	*U.S. $*	*Price Can. $*	*U.K. £*
Brown/white/orange/bronze	R-W	200.00	275.00	150.00

Note: Issued with a wooden plinth and a glass dome (8″ x 4″).

RW4272
PEREGRINE FALCON
Style One

Modeller: David Fryer
Height: 17 ½″, 44.5 cm
Colour: Brown, black and white china bird; bronze foliage; wooden base
Issued: 1983 in a limited edition of 150
Series: Ornamental Studio (Large size)

Colourways	*Backstamp*	*U.S. $*	*Price Can. $*	*U.K. £*
Brown/black/white/bronze	R-W	1,000.00	1,500.00	750.00

RW4283
MARSH TIT
Style Two

Modeller: David Fryer
Height: Unknown
Colour: Yellow, green and brown bird; yellow flowers; bronze foliage and base
Issued: 1986-1988
Series: British Birds on Bronze (Large size)

Colourways	*Backstamp*	*U.S. $*	*Price Can. $*	*U.K. £*
Yellow/green/brown/bronze	R-W	175.00	250.00	125.00

RW4284
GOLDEN EAGLE (AQUILA CHRYSAETOS)

Modeller: David Fryer
Height: 27″ x 39 ½″, 68.6 x 100.3 cm
Colour: Golden and dark brown bird (bone china); cast crystal base
Plinth: Wooden (mahogany)
Issued: 1986 in a limited edition of 15
Series: Ornamental Studio (Large size)

Colourways	*Backstamp*	*U.S. $*	*Price Can. $*	*U.K. £*
Golden/brown/crystal	R-W		Extremely rare	

Note: This model, the largest ever produced by Royal Worcester, has a cast crystal base and a 48″ wooden plinth. Due to firing problems only five models were produced.

RW4287
REED WARBLER

Modeller: David Fryer
Height: Unknown
Colour: Brown, white and black bird; green acorns; bronze foliage and base
Issued: 1986-1988
Series: British Birds on Bronze (Large size)

Colourways	*Backstamp*	*U.S. $*	*Price Can. $*	*U.K. £*
Brown/white/black/bronze	R-W	175.00	250.00	125.00

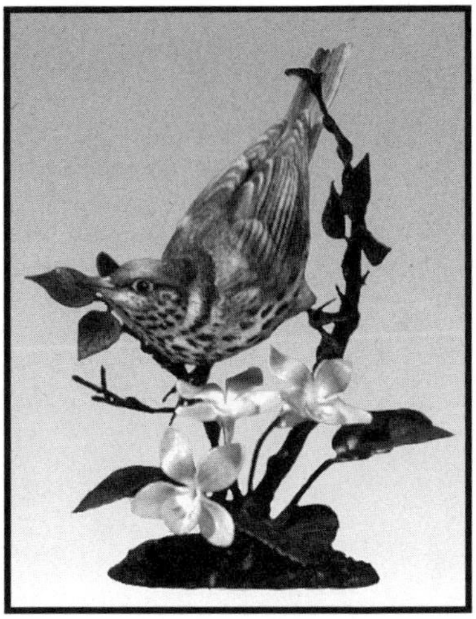

RW4289
THRUSH
Style Two

Modeller: David Fryer
Height: Unknown
Colour: Brown bird; purple flowers; bronze foliage and base
Issued: 1986-1988
Series: British Birds on Bronze (Large size)

			Price	
Colourways	*Backstamp*	*U.S. $*	*Can. $*	*U.K. £*
Brown/purple/bronze	R-W	175.00	250.00	125.00

RW4290
CHAFFINCH
Style Two

Modeller: David Fryer
Height: Unknown
Colour: Orange, blue, black and white bird; pink flowers; bronze foliage and base
Issued: 1986-1988
Series: British Birds on Bronze (Large size)

			Price	
Colourways	*Backstamp*	*U.S. $*	*Can. $*	*U.K. £*
Orange/blue/pink/bronze	R-W	175.00	250.00	125.00

RW4318
CAT (Seated)

Modeller: Carol Gladman
Height: Unknown
Colour:
1. Black
2. Black with white nose, bib and paws
3. Ginger and white
4. Tabby
5. Tortoiseshell

Issued: 1985
Series: Severn Street Cats

			Price	
Colourways	*Backstamp*	*U.S. $*	*Can. $*	*U.K. £*
Coloured (as above)	Black	100.00	135.00	75.00

Note: Sold at Severn Street factory site only.

RW4319
TABBY KITTEN (Seated)

Modeller: Carol Gladman
Height: Unknown
Colour: 1. Black with white nose, bib and tail
2. Ginger and white
3. Tabby
4. Tortoiseshell
5. White
Issued: 1985
Series: Severn Street Cats

			Price	
Colourways	*Backstamp*	*U.S. $*	*Can. $*	*U.K. £*
Coloured (as above)	Black	100.00	135.00	75.00

Note: Sold at Severn Street factory site only.

RW4320
KITTEN (Lying)
Style Two

Modeller: Carol Gladman
Height: Unknown
Colour: 1. Black and white
2. Ginger and white
3. Tabby
4. Tortoiseshell
5. White
Issued: 1985
Series: Severn Street Cats

			Price	
Colourways	*Backstamp*	*U.S. $*	*Can. $*	*U.K. £*
Coloured (as above)	Black	100.00	135.00	75.00

Note: Sold at Severn Street factory site only.

RW4332
AMERICAN ROBIN ON BRONZE

Modeller: James Alder
Height: Unknown
Colour: Brown and red bird; red berries; bronze foliage
Issued: 1981

			Price	
Colourways	*Backstamp*	*U.S. $*	*Can. $*	*U.K. £*
Brown/red/bronze	R-W	175.00	250.00	125.00

RW4337
SYMBOLI RUDOLF (WINNER OF THE TRIPLE CROWN IN JAPAN)

Modeller: Kenneth Potts
Height: Unknown
Colour: Chestnut
Plinth: Wooden
Issued: 1987 in a limited edition of 250
Series: Japanese Thoroughbreds

Colourways	*Backstamp*	*U.S. $*	*Price* *Can. $*	*U.K. £*
Chestnut	Black	1,000.00	1,500.00	750.00

Note: Commissioned for the Japanese market by Barbizon.

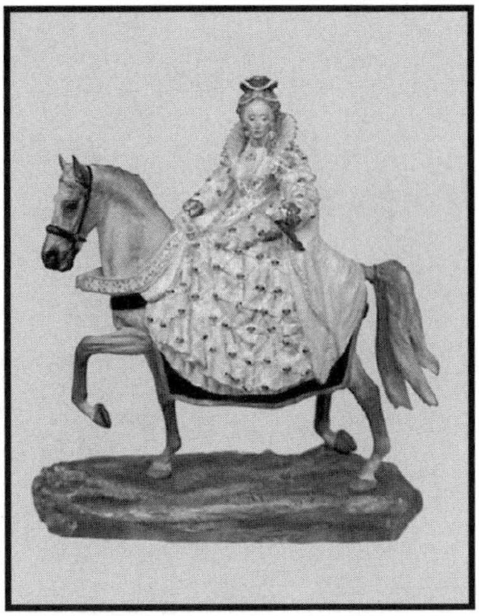

RW4356
QUEEN ELIZABETH I

Modeller: Kenneth Potts
Height: 15 ½", 39.4 cm
Colour: Creamy-white gown and cape; gold decoration; burgundy cap; grey horse; blue and gold saddle cloth
Plinth: Wooden
Issued: 1998 in a limited edition of 100

Colourways	*Backstamp*	*U.S. $*	*Price* *Can. $*	*U.K. £*
Creamy-white/gold/grey/blue	Black	—	—	7,085.00

RW4498
HENRY VIII

Modeller: Kenneth Potts
Height: 15 ½", 39.4 cm
Colour: Burgundy cape; grey tunic; white stockings; bay horse; green reins and riding cloth
Plinth: Wooden
Issued: 1991 in a limited edition of 75

Colourways	*Backstamp*	*U.S. $*	*Price* *Can. $*	*U.K. £*
Burgundy/grey/white/bay	Black	—	—	8,105.00

RW4500
OGURI CAP

Modeller: Kenneth Potts
Height: Unknown
Colour: Dark grey and black
Plinth: Wooden
Issued: 1991 in a limited edition of 100
Series: Japanese Thoroughbreds

Colourways	*Backstamp*	*U.S. $*	*Price* *Can. $*	*U.K. £*
Dark grey/black	Black	1,000.00	1,500.00	750.00

Note: Issued for the Japanese market.

RW4536
THE ROYAL TOURNAMENT

Modeller: David Lovegrove
Height: 5″, 12.7 cm
Colour: Blue; white circular base with blue trim
Issued: 1992

Colourways	*Backstamp*	*U.S. $*	*Price* *Can. $*	*U.K. £*
Blue/white	Black	100.00	135.00	75.00

RW4546
ARAB STALLION (and Rider)

Modeller: Kenneth Potts
Height: 16″, 40.6 cm
Colour: Rider: Multicoloured
Horse: Grey
Plinth: Wooden
Issued: 1993 in a limited edition of 50
Series: Classic Horse and Rider

Colourways	*Backstamp*	*U.S. $*	*Price* *Can. $*	*U.K. £*
Multicoloured	Black	—	—	6,745.00

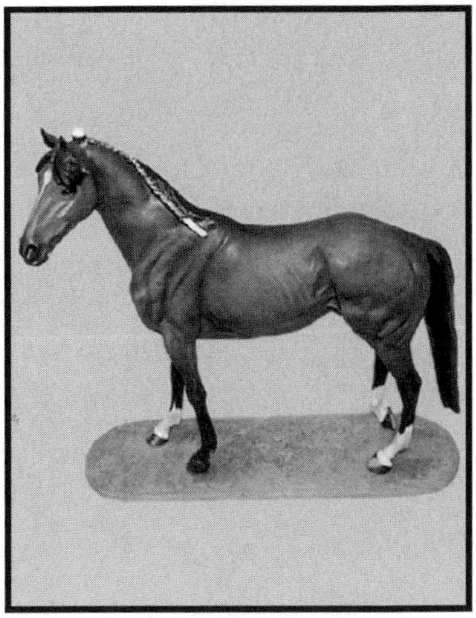

RW4578
TAKAI TEIO

Modeller: Kenneth Potts
Height: Unknown
Colour: Brown with black markings
Issued: 1990 in a limited edition of 75
Series: Japanese Thoroughbreds

			Price	
Colourways	*Backstamp*	*U.S. $*	*Can. $*	*U.K. £*
Brown/black/white	Black	1,000.00	1,500.00	750.00

Note: Issued for the Japanese market.

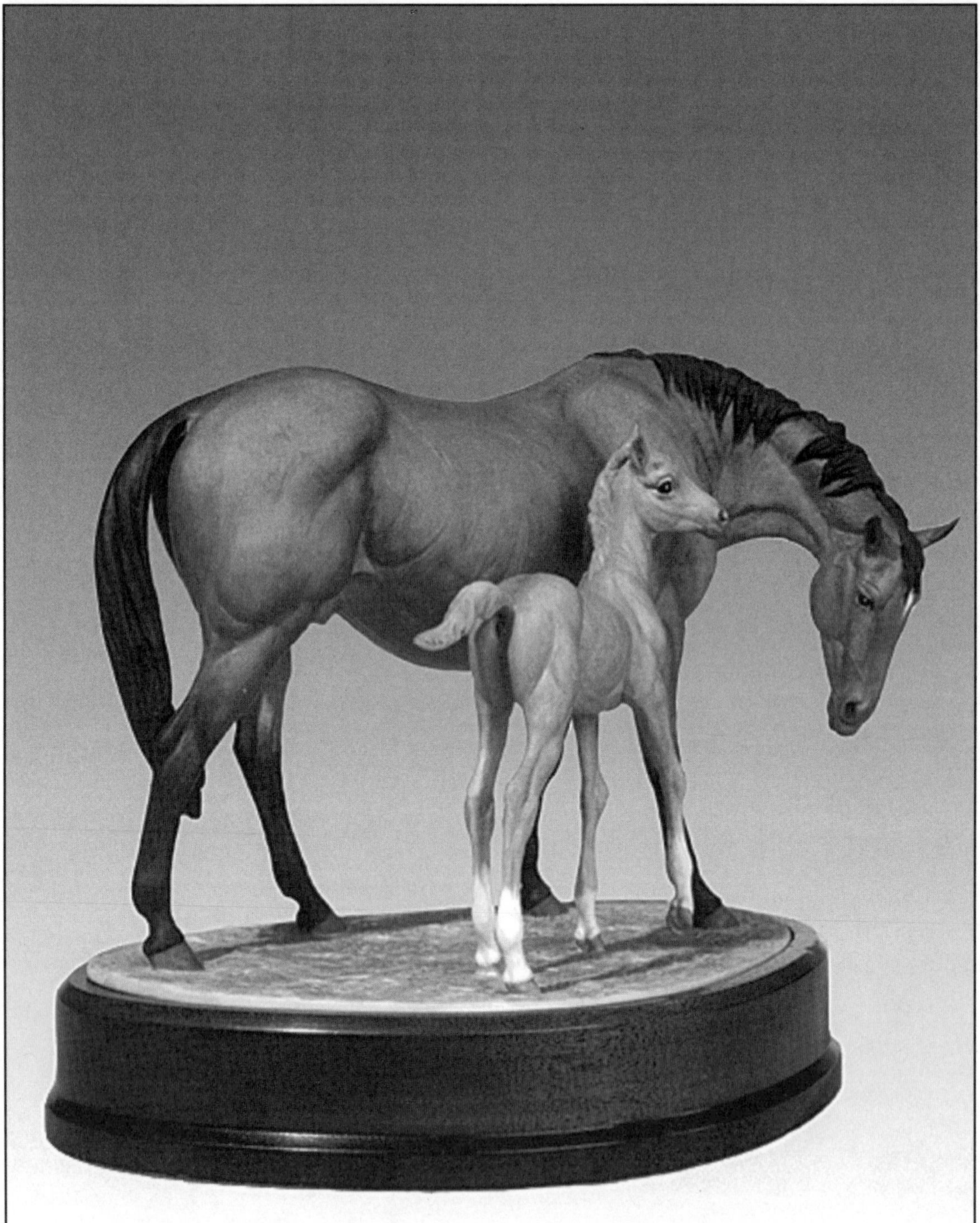

RW3871 Prince's Grace and Foal

ANIMAL BROOCHES AND MENU HOLDERS

RW3900 Wren on Bronze, Style One

RW2953
FOXHOUND (Walking) MENU HOLDER

Modeller: Doris Lindner
Height: 2 ½", 6.4 cm
Colour: White with brown markings
Issued: 1932

Description	*Backstamp*	*U.S. $*	*Price Can. $*	*U.K. £*
Menu holder	Puce	350.00	450.00	200.00

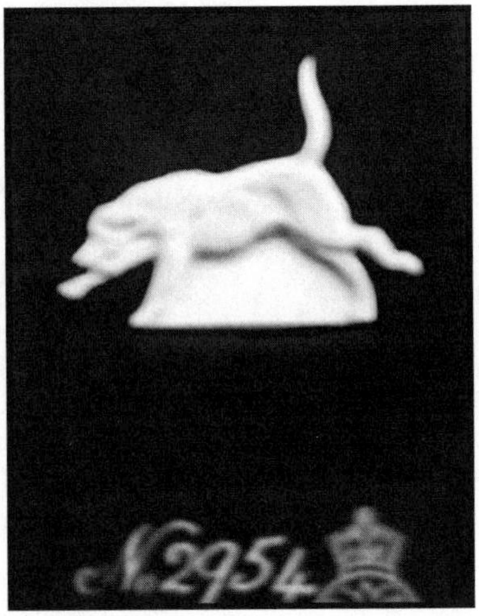

RW2954
FOXHOUND (Running) MENU HOLDER

Modeller: Doris Lindner
Height: 2 ¾", 7.0 cm
Colour: White with brown markings
Issued: 1932

Description	*Backstamp*	*U.S. $*	*Price Can. $*	*U.K. £*
Menu holder	Puce	350.00	450.00	200.00

RW2955
FOXHOUND (Seated) MENU HOLDER

Modeller: Doris Lindner
Height: 2 ¼", 5.7 cm
Colour: 1. Coloured
2. White
Issued: 1932

Colourways	*Backstamp*	*U.S. $*	*Price Can. $*	*U.K. £*
1. Coloured	Puce	375.00	500.00	225.00
2. White	Green	275.00	375.00	175.00

RW2956
FOX (Walking) MENU HOLDER

Modeller: Doris Lindner
Height: 2 ¼", 5.7 cm
Colour: Reddish-brown fox; beige menu holder
Issued: 1932

Description	*Backstamp*	*U.S. $*	*Price* *Can. $*	*U.K. £*
Menu holder	Puce	350.00	450.00	200.00

RW2957
FOX (Stalking) BROOCH / MENU HOLDER

Modeller: Doris Lindner
Height: 2 ½", 6.4 cm
Colour: Reddish-brown
Issued: 1932

Description	*Backstamp*	*U.S. $*	*Price* *Can. $*	*U.K. £*
1. Brooch	Puce	400.00	550.00	250.00
2. Menu holder	Puce	350.00	450.00	200.00

RW2958
SEALYHAM TERRIER BROOCH / MENU HOLDER

Modeller: Unknown
Height: 2", 5.0 cm
Colour: Cream with reddish-brown face and ears
Issued: 1932

Description	*Backstamp*	*U.S. $*	*Price* *Can. $*	*U.K. £*
1. Brooch	Puce	400.00	550.00	250.00
2. Menu holder	Puce	350.00	450.00	200.00

RW2959
AIREDALE TERRIER BROOCH / MENU HOLDER

Modeller: Unknown
Height: 2", 5.0 cm
Colour: Reddish-brown with black markings
Issued: 1932

Description	*Backstamp*	*U.S. $*	*Price Can. $*	*U.K. £*
1. Brooch	Puce	400.00	550.00	250.00
2. Menu holder	Puce	350.00	475.00	200.00

RW2960
DANDIE DINMONT BROOCH

Modeller: Unknown
Height: 2", 5.0 cm
Colour: Grey, cream and reddish-brown
Issued: 1932

Description	*Backstamp*	*U.S. $*	*Price Can. $*	*U.K. £*
Brooch	Puce	400.00	550.00	250.00

RW2961
COCKER SPANIEL BROOCH / MENU HOLDER

Modeller: Unknown
Height: 2", 5.0 cm
Colour: 1. Black
2. Liver and white
Issued: 1932

Description	*Backstamp*	*U.S. $*	*Price Can. $*	*U.K. £*
1. Brooch	Puce	400.00	550.00	250.00
2. Menu holder	Puce	350.00	450.00	200.00

RW2962
FIELD SPANIEL BROOCH / MENU HOLDER

Modeller: Unknown
Height: 2", 5.0 cm
Colour: Black
Issued: 1932

Description	Backstamp	U.S. $	Price Can. $	U.K. £
1. Brooch	Puce	400.00	550.00	250.00
2. Menu holder	Puce	350.00	450.00	200.00

RW2963
COLLIE BROOCH

Modeller: Unknown
Height: 2", 5.0 cm
Colour: Brown and white
Issued: 1932

Description	Backstamp	U.S. $	Price Can. $	U.K. £
Brooch	Puce	400.00	550.00	250.00

RW2964
PEKINESE BROOCH / MENU HOLDER

Modeller: Unknown
Height: 2", 5.0 cm
Colour: Light reddish-brown
Issued: 1932

Description	Backstamp	U.S. $	Price Can. $	U.K. £
1. Brooch	Puce	400.00	550.00	250.00
2. Menu holder	Puce	350.00	450.00	200.00

RW2965
CAIRN BROOCH

Modeller: Unknown
Height: 2 ½", 6.4 cm
Colour: Brown
Issued: 1932

Description	*Backstamp*	*U.S. $*	*Price Can. $*	*U.K. £*
Brooch	Puce	400.00	550.00	250.00

RW2966
SETTER BROOCH / MENU HOLDER

Modeller: Unknown
Height: 2", 5.0 cm
Colour: Chestnut red
Issued: 1932

Description	*Backstamp*	*U.S. $*	*Price Can. $*	*U.K. £*
1. Brooch	Puce	400.00	550.00	250.00
2. Menu holder	Puce	350.00	450.00	200.00

RW2967
DACHSHUND BROOCH

Modeller: Unknown
Height: 2", 5.0 cm
Colour: Reddish-brown
Issued: 1932

Description	*Backstamp*	*U.S. $*	*Price Can. $*	*U.K. £*
Brooch	Puce	400.00	550.00	250.00

Photograph not available at press time

RW2969
WEST HIGHLAND TERRIER BROOCH

Modeller: Unknown
Height: 2″, 5.0 cm
Colour: Unknown
Issued: 1932

Description	*Backstamp*	*U.S. $*	*Price Can. $*	*U.K. £*
Brooch	Puce	400.00	550.00	250.00

RW2970
WIRE-HAIRED TERRIER BROOCH

Modeller: Unknown
Height: 2″, 5.0 cm
Colour: White with reddish-brown and black patches
Issued: 1932

Description	*Backstamp*	*U.S. $*	*Price Can. $*	*U.K. £*
Brooch	Puce	400.00	550.00	250.00

RW2971
ALSATIAN BROOCH / MENU HOLDER

Modeller: Unknown
Height: 2″, 5.0 cm
Colour: Brown with darker brown shading
Issued: 1932

Description	*Backstamp*	*U.S. $*	*Price Can. $*	*U.K. £*
1. Brooch	Puce	400.00	550.00	250.00
2. Menu holder	Puce	350.00	450.00	200.00

RW2972
SCOTTISH TERRIER BROOCH / MENU HOLDER

Modeller: Unknown
Height: 2″, 5.0 cm
Colour: White
Issued: 1932

Description	*Backstamp*	*U.S. $*	*Price Can. $*	*U.K. £*
1. Brooch	Puce	400.00	550.00	250.00
2. Menu holder	Puce	350.00	450.00	200.00

RW2973
FOXHOUND BROOCH

Modeller: Frederick M. Gertner
Height: 2″, 5.0 cm
Colour: Unknown
Issued: 1932

Description	*Backstamp*	*U.S. $*	*Price Can. $*	*U.K. £*
Brooch	Puce	400.00	550.00	250.00

RW2974
CHOW BROOCH

Modeller: Unknown
Height: 2″, 5.0 cm
Colour: Reddish-brown
Issued: 1932

Description	*Backstamp*	*U.S. $*	*Price Can. $*	*U.K. £*
Brooch	Puce	400.00	550.00	250.00

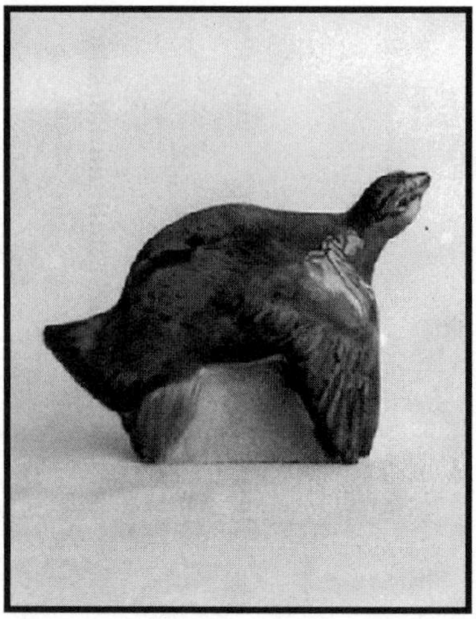

RW2975
GROUSE BROOCH

Modeller: Frederick M. Gertner
Height: 2", 5.0 cm
Colour: Reddish-brown
Issued: 1932

Description	*Backstamp*	*U.S. $*	*Price Can. $*	*U.K. £*
Brooch	Puce	350.00	450.00	200.00

RW2976
SNIPE BROOCH

Modeller: Frederick M. Gertner
Height: 2 ½", 6.4 cm
Colour: Brown and cream; green base
Issued: 1932

Description	*Backstamp*	*U.S. $*	*Price Can. $*	*U.K. £*
Brooch	Puce	350.00	450.00	200.00

RW2977
BULLFINCH BROOCH

Modeller: Frederick M. Gertner
Height: 2", 5.0 cm
Colour: Red and black
Issued: 1932

Description	*Backstamp*	*U.S. $*	*Price Can. $*	*U.K. £*
Brooch	Puce	350.00	450.00	200.00

RW2978
SPARROWHAWK BROOCH

Modeller: Frederick M. Gertner
Height: 2", 5.0 cm
Colour: Unknown
Issued: 1932

Description	Backstamp	U.S. $	Price Can. $	U.K. £
Brooch	Puce	350.00	450.00	200.00

RW2979
PARROQUET BROOCH

Modeller: Frederick M. Gertner
Height: 2", 5.0 cm
Colour: Unknown
Issued: 1932

Description	Backstamp	U.S. $	Price Can. $	U.K. £
Brooch	Puce	350.00	450.00	200.00

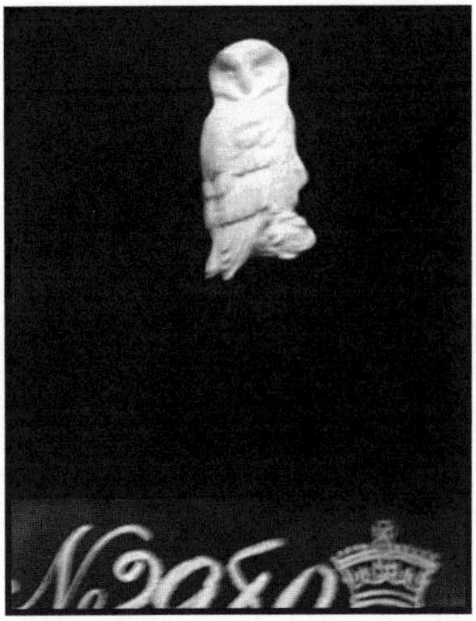

RW2980
OWL BROOCH

Modeller: Frederick M. Gertner
Height: 2", 5.0 cm
Colour: Unknown
Issued: 1932

Description	Backstamp	U.S. $	Price Can. $	U.K. £
Brooch	Puce	350.00	450.00	200.00

RW2981
SWALLOW BROOCH

Modeller: Frederick M. Gertner
Height: 2", 5.0 cm
Colour: Brown
Issued: 1932

Description	*Backstamp*	*U.S. $*	*Price Can. $*	*U.K. £*
Brooch	Puce	350.00	450.00	200.00

RW2982
ROBIN BROOCH

Modeller: Frederick M. Gertner
Height: 2", 5.0 cm
Colour: Brown and red
Issued: 1932

Description	*Backstamp*	*U.S. $*	*Price Can. $*	*U.K. £*
Brooch	Puce	350.00	450.00	200.00

RW2983
BLACKCOCK BROOCH

Modeller: Frederick M. Gertner
Height: 2 ½", 6.4 cm
Colour: Black with dark brown markings
Issued: 1932

Description	*Backstamp*	*U.S. $*	*Price Can. $*	*U.K. £*
Brooch	Puce	350.00	450.00	200.00

RW2984
QUAIL BROOCH

Modeller: Frederick M. Gertner
Height: 1 ¾", 4.4 cm
Colour: Brown and cream
Issued: 1932

Description	Backstamp	U.S. $	Price Can. $	U.K. £
Brooch	Puce	350.00	450.00	200.00

RW2985
WILD DUCK BROOCH

Modeller: Frederick M. Gertner
Height: 2 ½", 6.4 cm
Colour: Green and browns
Issued: 1932

Description	Backstamp	U.S. $	Price Can. $	U.K. £
Brooch	Puce	350.00	450.00	200.00

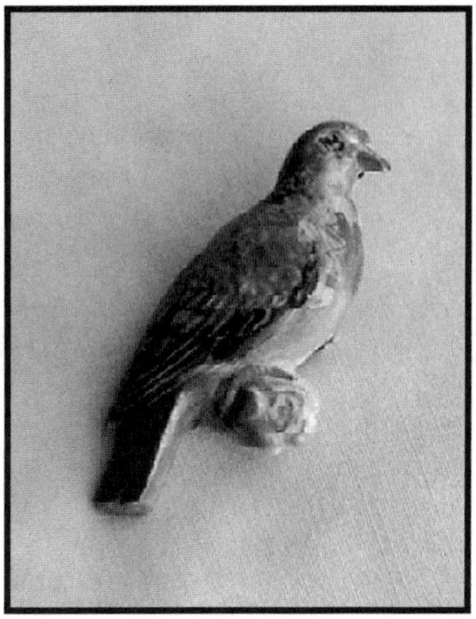

RW2986
WOOD PIGEON BROOCH

Modeller: Frederick M. Gertner
Height: 2 ½", 6.4 cm
Colour: Grey and red
Issued: 1932

Description	Backstamp	U.S. $	Price Can. $	U.K. £
Brooch	Puce	350.00	450.00	200.00

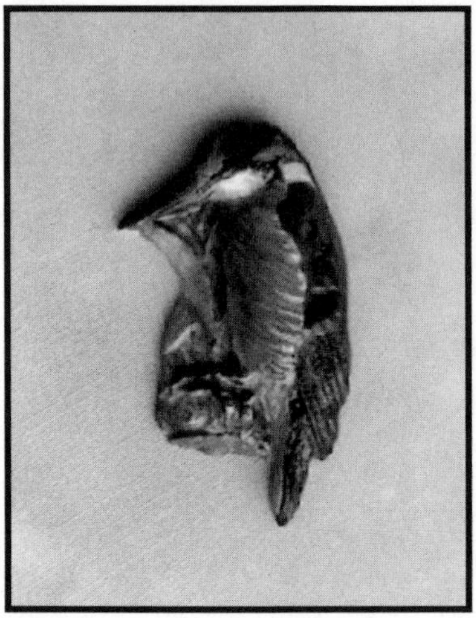

RW2987
KINGFISHER BROOCH

Modeller: Frederick M. Gertner
Height: 2 ½", 6.4 cm
Colour: Teal blue and dark red
Issued: 1932

Description	*Backstamp*	*U.S. $*	*Price* *Can. $*	*U.K. £*
Brooch	Puce	350.00	450.00	200.00

RW2988
PHEASANT BROOCH / MENU HOLDER

Modeller: Frederick M. Gertner
Height: 2 ½", 6.4 cm
Colour: Browns
Issued: 1932

Description	*Backstamp*	*U.S. $*	*Price* *Can. $*	*U.K. £*
1. Brooch	Puce	350.00	450.00	200.00
2. Menu holder	Puce	350.00	450.00	200.00

RW2989
PENGUIN BROOCH

Modeller: Frederick M. Gertner
Height: 2 ½", 6.4 cm
Colour: Black and white with orange beak
Issued: 1932

Description	*Backstamp*	*U.S. $*	*Price* *Can. $*	*U.K. £*
Brooch	Puce	350.00	450.00	200.00

RW2990
WOODCOCK BROOCH

Modeller: Frederick M. Gertner
Height: 2″, 5.0 cm
Colour: Unknown
Issued: 1932

Description	Backstamp	U.S. $	Price Can. $	U.K. £
Brooch	Puce	350.00	450.00	200.00

RW2991
JAY BROOCH

Modeller: Frederick M. Gertner
Height: 2″, 5.0 cm
Colour: Blue
Issued: 1932

Description	Backstamp	U.S. $	Price Can. $	U.K. £
Brooch	Puce	350.00	450.00	200.00

RW2992
SEAGULL BROOCH

Modeller: Frederick M. Gertner
Height: 2″, 5.0 cm
Colour: White
Issued: 1932

Description	Backstamp	U.S. $	Price Can. $	U.K. £
Brooch	Puce	350.00	450.00	200.00

RW2995
GOLDEN PHEASANT BROOCH

Modeller: Possibly Frederick M. Gertner
Height: 2", 5.0 cm
Colour: Browns
Issued: 1932

Description	*Backstamp*	*U.S. $*	*Price Can. $*	*U.K. £*
Brooch	Puce	350.00	450.00	200.00

RW2996
LADY AMHERST'S PHEASANT BROOCH

Modeller: Possibly Frederick M. Gertner
Height: 2", 5.0 cm
Colour: Unknown
Issued: 1932

Description	*Backstamp*	*U.S. $*	*Price Can. $*	*U.K. £*
Brooch	Puce	350.00	450.00	200.00

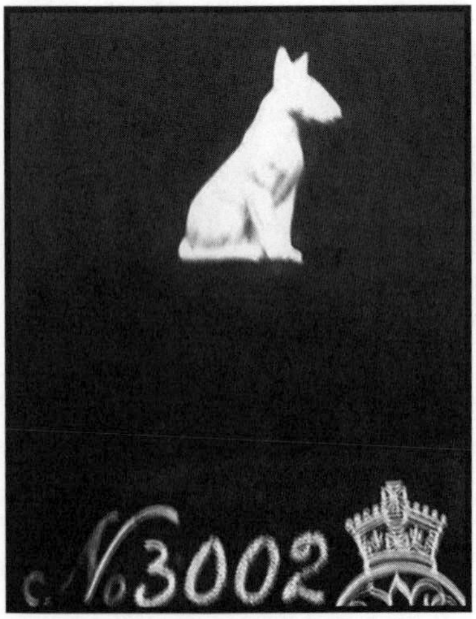

RW3002
BULL TERRIER BROOCH

Modeller: Unknown
Height: 2", 5.0 cm
Colour: White
Issued: 1932

Description	*Backstamp*	*U.S. $*	*Price Can. $*	*U.K. £*
Brooch	Puce	400.00	550.00	250.00

RW3003
BEDLINGTON TERRIER BROOCH

Modeller: Unknown
Height: 2", 5.0 cm
Colour: Unknown
Issued: 1932

Description	*Backstamp*	*U.S. $*	*Price Can. $*	*U.K. £*
Brooch	Puce	400.00	550.00	250.00

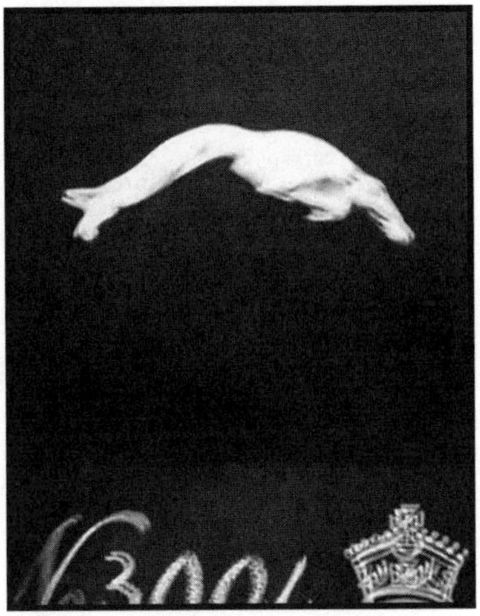

RW3004
GREYHOUND BROOCH

Modeller: Unknown
Height: 2 ½", 6.4 cm
Colour: Tan
Issued: 1932

Description	*Backstamp*	*U.S. $*	*Price Can. $*	*U.K. £*
Brooch	Puce	400.00	550.00	250.00

RW3005
DALMATIAN BROOCH

Modeller: Unknown
Height: 2 ½", 6.4 cm
Colour: White with black spots
Issued: 1932

Description	*Backstamp*	*U.S. $*	*Price Can. $*	*U.K. £*
Brooch	Puce	400.00	550.00	250.00

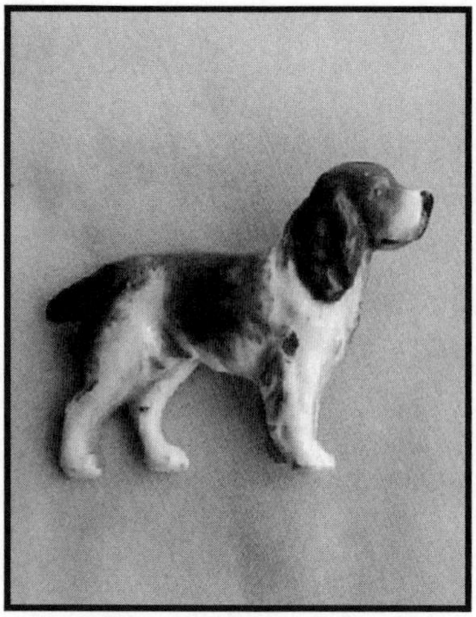

RW3007
SPRINGER SPANIEL BROOCH

Modeller: Unknown
Height: 2″, 5.0 cm
Colour: White with reddish-brown markings
Issued: 1933

Description	*Backstamp*	*U.S. $*	*Price* *Can. $*	*U.K. £*
Brooch	Puce	400.00	550.00	250.00

EQUINE STUDIES

RW3880 American Saddle Horse

AETHON

Modeller: Doris Lindner
Height: 5″, 12.7 cm
Colour: 1. White
2. White with tan markings
Issued: 1. 1982
2. 1983
Series: Equine Studies

Colourways	*Backstamp*	*U.S. $*	*Price Can. $*	*U.K. £*
1. White	Black	100.00	135.00	75.00
2. White/tan	Black	60.00	80.00	45.00

ASTROPE

Modeller: Doris Lindner
Height: 5″, 12.7 cm
Colour: 1. White
2. White with grey markings
Issued: 1. 1982
2. 1983
Series: Equine Studies

Colourways	*Backstamp*	*U.S. $*	*Price Can. $*	*U.K. £*
1. White	Black	100.00	135.00	75.00
2. White/grey	Black	60.00	80.00	45.00

BRONTE

Modeller: Doris Lindner
Height: 5″, 12.7 cm
Colour: 1. White
2. White with grey markings
Issued: 1. 1982
2. 1983
Series: Equine Studies

Colourways	*Backstamp*	*U.S. $*	*Price Can. $*	*U.K. £*
1. White	Black	100.00	135.00	75.00
2. White/grey	Black	60.00	80.00	45.00

CHRONOS

Modeller: Doris Lindner
Height: 5", 12.7 cm
Colour: 1. White
2. White with grey mane
Issued: 1. 1982
2. 1983
Series: Equine Studies

Colourways	Backstamp	U.S. $	Price Can. $	U.K. £
1. White	Black	100.00	135.00	75.00
2. White/grey	Black	60.00	80.00	45.00

EOUS

Modeller: Doris Lindner
Height: 5", 12.7 cm
Colour: 1. White
2. White with brown face and neck
Issued: 1. 1982
2. 1983
Series: Equine Studies

Colourways	Backstamp	U.S. $	Price Can. $	U.K. £
1. White	Black	100.00	135.00	75.00
2. White/brown	Black	60.00	80.00	45.00

LAMPON

Modeller: Doris Lindner
Height: 5", 12.7 cm
Colour: 1. White
2. White with grey markings
Issued: 1. 1982
2. 1983
Series: Equine Studies

Colourways	Backstamp	U.S. $	Price Can. $	U.K. £
1. White	Black	100.00	135.00	75.00
2. White/grey	Black	60.00	80.00	45.00

PHAETHON

Modeller: Doris Lindner
Height: 5", 12.7 cm
Colour: 1. White
2. White with light tan shading
Issued: 1. 1982
2. 1983
Series: Equine Studies

Colourways	Backstamp	Price U.S. $	Can. $	U.K. £
1. White	Black	100.00	135.00	75.00
2. White/tan	Black	60.00	80.00	45.00

PHLEGON

Modeller: Doris Lindner
Height: 5", 12.7 cm
Colour: 1. White
2. White with brown face and neck; darker brown mane
Issued: 1. 1982
2. 1983
Series: Equine Studies

Colourways	Backstamp	Price U.S. $	Can. $	U.K. £
1. White	Black	100.00	135.00	75.00
2. White/brown	Black	60.00	80.00	45.00

PYROESIS

Modeller: Doris Lindner
Height: 5", 12.7 cm
Colour: 1. White
2. White with pale brown face and neck
Issued: 1. 1982
2. 1983
Series: Equine Studies

Colourways	Backstamp	Price U.S. $	Can. $	U.K. £
1. White	Black	100.00	135.00	75.00
2. White/brown	Black	60.00	80.00	45.00

RW4048 Linnet on Wild Rose

COLLECTING BY SERIES

ALICE IN WONDERLAND

Cheshire Cat	RW3609
The Dodo	RW3613
Mock Turtle	RW3610
White Rabbit	RW3611

For "Alice" see *The Charlton Standard Catalogue of Royal Worcester Figurines*

AMERICAN BIRDS (Small)

American Robin	RW3647
Blue Jay	RW3646
Bluebird	RW3649
Cardinal	RW3645
Wax Wing	RW3648
Western Tanager	RW3650

AMERICAN BIRDS BY DOROTHY DOUGHTY

American Goldfinch and Thistle	
Cock	RW3134
Hen	RW3135
American Redstart	
Cock	RW3112
Hen	RW3113
Audubon Warbler and Palo Verdi	
Cock	RW3669
Hen	RW3670
Baltimore Oriole and Tulip Tree	
Cock	RW3268
Hen	RW3269
Bewick's Wren and Yellow Jasmine	
Cock	RW3512
Hen	RW3513
Bluebird and Apple Blossom	
Cock	RW3137
Hen	RW3136
Blue-Grey Gnatcatcher and Dogwood	
Double	RW3507
Single	RW3506
Bob-White Quail, Style One	
Cock	RW3323
Hen	RW3324
Cactus Wren and Prickly Pear	
Cock	RW3618
Hen	RW3619
Canyon Wren and Wild Lupin	
Cock	RW3639
Hen	RW3640
Cerulean Warbler and Red Maple	
Cock	RW3659
Hen	RW3660
Chickadee and Larch	
Cock	RW3241
Hen	RW3242
Downy Woodpecker and Pecan	
Cock	RW3592
Hen	RW3593
Elf Owl and Saguaro	RW3617
Extinct Carolina Paroquets	RW3632
Golden-Crowned Kinglet and Noble Pine	
Double	RW3468
Single	RW3467
Hooded Warbler and Cherokee Rose	
Cock	RW3590
Hen	RW3591
Indigo Bunting and Blackberry	
Cock	RW3367
Hen	RW3368
Indigo Bunting on Plum Tree (Single)	RW3223
Lark Sparrow with Twin Pod and Red Gila	RW3686
Lazuli Bunting and Choke Cherry	
Cock	RW3651
Hen	RW3652
Magnolia Warbler and Magnolia	
Cock	RW3430
Hen	RW3429
Mockingbird and Peach Blossom	
Cock	RW3326
Hen	RW3327
Mountain Bluebird and Spleenwort Niger	
Cock	RW3665
Hen	RW3666
Myrtle Warbler and Weeping Cherry	
Cock	RW3508
Hen	RW3509
Ovenbird with Crested Iris (Hen)	RW3533
Ovenbird with Lady's Slipper (Cock)	RW3532
Parula Warbler and Sweet Bay	
Cock	RW3536
Hen	RW3537
Phoebe and Flame Vine	
Cock	RW3548
Hen	RW3549
Red-Eyed Vireo and Swamp Azalea	
Cock	RW3469
Hen	RW3470
Ruby-Throated Hummingbird and Fuchsia	
Cock	RW3438
Hen	RW3439
Scarlet Tanager and White Oak	
Cock	RW3525
Hen	RW3526
Scissor-Tailed Flycatchers	RW3627
Vermilion Flycatcher and Pussy Willow	
Cock	RW3657
Hen	RW3658
Virginia Cardinal and Orange Blossom	
Cock	RW3190
Hen	RW3191
Yellow-Headed Blackbird and Spiderwort	
Cock	RW3464
Hen	RW3465
Yellow-Throat and Water Hyacinth	
Cock	RW3539
Hen	RW3540

AMERICAN BIRDS ON BRONZE (Small)

Bluebird and Pine Cones	RW4186
Carolina Wren and Wild Rose	RW4178
Chickadee and Daisies	RW4181
Red Cardinal on Bronze	RW4180
Robin and Narcissus	RW4179

BIRDS OF PREY ON BRONZE (Small)

Bald Eagle	RW4270
Barn Owl	RW4241
Kestrel	RW4240
Marsh Harrier	RW4246
Peregrine Falcon, Style Two	RW4243
Short-eared Owl	RW4260

BIRDS ON STUMPS

Bullfinch	RW2662
Canary	RW2665
Goldfinch	RW2667
Kingfisher	RW2666
Parroquet (Female), Style One	RW2663
Parrot (Male)	RW2664

BRITISH BIRDS

Series One

Blue Tit	RW3199
Bullfinch	RW3238
Chaffinch, Style One	RW3240
Goldcrest	RW3338
Goldfinch	RW3239
Great Tit	RW3335
Hedge Sparrow	RW3333
Jay	RW3248
Kingfisher	RW3235
Marsh Tit, Style One	RW3336
Nightingale	RW3337
Nuthatch	RW3334
Robin	RW3197
Sparrow	RW3236
Thrush, Style One	RW3234
Wood Warbler	RW3200
Woodpecker	RW3249
Wren	RW3198

Series Two

Bearded Reedling	RW3961
Blue Tit on Hogweed	RW4029
Dartford Warbler	RW3960
Dippers	RW3965
Greenfinch on Beech	RW4061
Greenfinch on Forsythia	RW4057
Linnet on Wild Rose	RW4048
Little Owl on Ivy	RW4030
Marsh Tit on Daphne	RW4056
Redstart	RW4068
Robin on Christmas Rose	RW4018
Shorelark	RW3963
Snow Bunting	RW3962
Wall Creeper	RW3964
Woodwarbler on Cherry	RW4019
Yellow Bunting on Blackberry	RW4040

Series Three

Crested Tit	RW4078
Grey Wagtail	RW4070
Robin on Holly, Style One	RW4071
Stonechat	RW4077

BRITISH BIRDS BY DOROTHY DOUGHTY

Blue-Tit and Pussy Willow in Spring (Cock)	RW3708
Blue-Tit Bathing in an Old Willow Stump (Hen)	RW3709
Bullfinch and Blackthorne	RW3712
Chiffchaff on Hogweed	RW3723
English Redstart on Gorse (Hen)	RW3693
English Redstart on Gorse in Spring (Cock)	RW3692
Goldcrest and Larch	
Cock	RW3703
Hen	RW3704
Grey Wagtail and Celandine (Cock)	RW3690
Kingfisher and Autumn Beech (Cock)	RW3734
Lesser Whitethroat on Wild Rose	
Cock	RW3694
Hen	RW3695
Long-Tailed Tits on Flowering Larch	RW3735
Meadow Pipit and Silverweed (Cock)	RW3713
Moorhen Chick on Waterlily Pads	RW3726
Nightingale and Honeysuckle, Style One	RW3701
Robin in Autumn Woods	RW3707
Wren and Burnet Rose	
Cock	RW3696
Hen	RW3727

BRITISH BIRDS ON BRONZE

Large

Chaffinch, Style Two	RW4290
Marsh Tit, Style Two	RW4283
Merlin Hawk	RW3911
Peregrine Falcon, Style One	RW4272
Reed Warbler	RW4287
Thrush, Style Two	RW4289

Small

Blue Tit, Style Two	RW3903
Goldcrest, Style Two	RW3902
Kingfisher, Style One	RW3898
Robin, Style One	RW3901
Swallow	RW3899
Wren, Style One	RW3900

Miniature

Blue Tit, Style Three	RW3908
Goldcrest, Style Three	RW3909
Kingfisher, Style Two	RW3904
Nuthatch	RW3907
Robin, Style Two	RW3905
Wren, Style Two	RW3910

CLASSIC HORSE AND RIDER

Arab Stallion (and Rider)	RW4546

COUNTRY LIFE CAMEOS

Bumblebee	RW4264
Butterfly	RW4267
Fox, Style Two	RW4175
Foxhound (Standing), Style Three	RW4173
Frog	RW4198
Grasshopper	RW4265
Mallards	RW4176
Otter	RW4177
Pointer Sleeping	RW4172
Salmon, Style Three	RW4174
Snail, Style Two	RW4197
Stag Beetle	RW4196

DOGS

Large

Afghanistan Hound	RW3425
Alsatian, Style Two	RW3462
Borzoi, Style One	RW3426
English Setter	RW3463
Irish Setter	RW3463

Small

Aberdeen Toy Terrier (Standing)	RW2946
Airedale Terrier (Seated)	RW2942
Airedale Terrier (Standing, head to left)	RW3027
Airedale Terrier (Standing, head to right)	RW3026
Alsatian, Style One	RW3295
Cocker Spaniel	
Style One	RW2944
Style Two	RW3033
Dachshund	RW3294
Dalmatian	RW3293
Dandie Dinmont Terrier	RW2943
English Bulldog	RW2945
English Springer Spaniel (Standing)	RW2944
Pekinese (Seated)	RW3034
Pekinese (Standing)	RW2941
Scottish Terrier (Seated)	RW3029
Scottish Terrier (Standing)	RW2946
Sealyham Terrier	RW3028
Welsh Corgi	RW3243
Wire-Haired Terrier (Seated)	RW2942
Wire-Haired Terrier (Standing, head to left)	RW3027
Wire-Haired Terrier (Standing, head to right)	RW3026

DOUBLE BIRDS ON TREE STUMPS

Blue Tits	RW3375
Chaffinches	RW3364
Cole Tits	RW3376
Linnets	RW3365
Pied Woodpeckers	RW3363
Yellowhammers	RW3377

EQUESTRIAN

At the Meet	RW3114
Cantering to the Post	RW3117
Huntsman and Hounds	RW3115
Over the Sticks	RW3116

FINAL COLLECTION BY DORIS LINDNER

Boxer (Standing)	RW4093
Hunter	RW4096
Pony Stallion	RW4095
The Saluki	RW4094
Thoroughbred Foal	RW4106
Thoroughbred Mare	RW4107

FLEDGLINGS

Blue Tit Fledgling and Clematis	RW4004
Bullfinch Fledgling on Apple Blossom	RW4005
Goldfinch Fledgling and Thistle	RW4006
Great Tit Fledgling	RW4001
Robin Fledgling on Branch	RW4003
Wren Fledgling on Leaves	RW4002

GAME BIRDS

Bob-White Quail, Style Two	
Cock	RW3827
Hen	RW3828
Canvasback Duck	RW3831
Green-Winged Teal	RW3836
Mallard	
Drake	RW3813
Hen	RW3814
Pintail	
Drake	RW3833
Hen	RW3834
Ring-Necked Pheasant	
Cock	RW3818
Hen	RW3819

GOATS

Goat	
Head raised, with base	RW3125
Head raised, without base	RW3530
Licking hind leg, with base	RW3124
Licking hind leg, without base	RW3531
Kids at Play	
With base	RW3153
Without base	RW3517

HAWKS AND FALCONS

Kek (Kestrel)	RW3981
Sparrowhawk	RW4009

HEAVY HORSES

Clydesdale Stallion	RW3944
Percheron Stallion "Saltmarsh Silver Crest"	RW3786
Shire Stallion "Manor Premier King"	RW3759
Suffolk Punch "Beccles Warrender"	RW3825

JAPANESE THOROUGHBREDS

Oguri Cap	RW4500
Symboli Rudolf (Winner of the Triple Crown in Japan)	RW4337
Takai Teio	RW4578

KITTENS

Kitten (Lying), Style One	RW4020
Kitten (Seated)	RW4007
Persian Kitten (On hind legs)	RW4045
Persian Kitten (Seated)	RW4027
Siamese Kitten	RW4046
Tabby Kitten (Lying)	RW4047

MILITARY COMMANDERS

Alexander (The Great)	RW3956
The Duke of Marlborough	RW3914
The Duke of Wellington	RW3870
Napolean Bonaparte	RW3860
Eugéne de Beauharnais	RW4055
Richard Coeur de Lion	RW4034
Simón Bolivar	RW4076
Washington (George)	RW3897
William the Conqueror	RW4067

NATURE STUDIES

Blue Tit on Bronze, Style One	RW4117
Bullfinch on Bronze	RW4118
Goldcrest on Bronze, Style One	RW4116
Hedgehog on Bronze, Style One	RW4111
Nightingale on Honeysuckle, Style Two	RW4102
Robin on Holly, Style Two	RW4103
Waterlily and Butterfly	RW4108
Wren on Clematis	RW4101

NETSUKE ANIMALS

Ape	RW2612
Blackcock	RW2622
Cheetah	RW2606
Cow	RW2609
Double Mouse	RW2636
Fish	RW2611
Mouse	RW2610
Quail	RW2623
Rabbit	RW2607
Ram	RW2613
Snail, Style One	RW2605
Snake	RW2608
Toad	RW2624
Tortoise	RW2604

NORTH AMERICAN BIRDS

Carolina Wren and Trumpet Creeper	RW3994
Chestnut-Collared Longspur	RW3995
Dickcissel and Sunflower	RW3993
Red-Breasted Nuthatch and Oak	RW3997
Ruby-Crowned Kinglet and Cypress	RW3996
Rufous Hummingbird	RW3998

ORNAMENTAL STUDIO

Barn Owl (Tyto Albo)	RW4210
Golden Eagle (Aquila Chrysaetos)	RW4284
Peregrine Falcon, Style One	RW4272

PRIZE CATTLE

Aberdeen Angus Bull "Newhouse Jewlian Eric"	RW3697
Brahman Bull "J. D. H. de Ellary Manso"	RW3821
British Friesian Bull "Terling Trusty"	RW3746
Charolais Bull "Vaillant"	RW3824
Dairy Shorthorn Bull "Royal Event"	RW3781
Hereford Bull "Vern Inspiration"	RW3668
Jersey Bull "Leebarn Carlisle II"	RW3776
Jersey Cow "Bramley Zenora"	RW3689
Santa Gertrudis Bull "Prince"	RW3702

RACE HORSES

Arkle	RW3817
Mill Reef	RW3942
Nijinsky	RW3893
Red Rum	RW3955

RACING STUDIES

At the Start, Style One (No. 4)	RW3959A
At the Start, Style Two (No. 6)	RW3959B
By a Short Head	RW3948
Cheltenham	RW3952
Grundy with Pat Eddery Up	RW3982
Mistral and Lester Piggot	RW4015

SEVERN STREET CATS

Cat (Seated)	RW4318
Kitten (Lying), Style Two	RW4320
Tabby Kitten (Seated)	RW4319

SPORTING DOGS

Clumber Spaniel	
With base	RW3232
Without base	RW3311
Cocker Spaniel	
With base	RW3231
Without base	RW3310
English Pointer	
With base	RW3229
Without base	RW3308
English Springer Spaniel	
With base	RW3232
Golden Retriever	
With base	RW3230
Without base	RW3309
Irish Setter	
With base	RW3228
Labrador Retriever	
With base	RW3233
Without base	RW3312
Red Setter	
With base	RW3228
Without base	RW3307

SPORTING FISH

Blue Marlin	RW3778
Blue-Fin Tuna	RW3787
Dolphin	RW3753
Flying Fish	RW3722
Sail Fish	RW3721
Swordfish	RW3788
Tarpon	RW3751

TROPICAL FISH

Large

Blue Angel Fish, Style Two	RW3603
Four-Eyed Fish and Banded Butterfly	RW3577
Rainbow Parrot Fish	RW3606
Red Hind Fish, Style Two	RW3602
Rock Beauty Fish	RW3605
Spanish Hog and Sergeant-Major Fish	RW3578
Squirrel Fish	RW3604

Small

Blue Angel Fish, Style One	RW3574
Four-Eyed Butterfly Fish	RW3573
Red Hind Fish, Style One	RW3572
Sergeant-Major Fish	RW3575
Spade Fish	RW3579
Yellow Grunt Fish	RW3576

WALL MOUNTS

Bulldog, Dog's Head	RW3320
Fox Head	RW3024
Hound Head	RW3025
Pekinese, Dog's Head	RW3322
Scottish Terrier, Dog's Head	RW3319
Spaniel, Dog's Head	RW3321

WOODLAND ANIMALS ON BRONZE

Dormouse	RW4237
Fox	RW4219
Hare	RW4211
Harvest Mouse	RW4209
Hedgehog, Style Two	RW4212
Red Squirrel	RW4238

ZOO BABIES

Bears, Mick and Mack	
With base	RW3265
Without base	RW3315
Fawns, Young Spotted Dear	
Oval base	RW3316
Rectangular base	RW3266
Without base	RW3529
Koala Bears, Billy Bluegums	
With base	RW3273
Without base	RW3317
Leopards, Nelson and Norah	
With base	RW3263
Without base	RW3313
Lions, Oliver and October	
With base	RW3264
Without base	RW3314
Tigers, Maurice and Sonia	
With base	RW3274
Without base	RW3318

INDEX

A

B

C

D

E

F

G

H

M

N

O

P

T

V

W

RW4027 Persian Kitten (Seated)